INTERNATIONAL SERIES OF MONOGRAPHS ON

ELECTRONICS AND INSTRUMENTATION

GENERAL EDITORS: D. W. FRY AND W. HIGINBOTHAM

VOLUME 24

TRANSIENT PHENOMENA
IN
ELECTRICAL POWER SYSTEMS

TRANSIENT PHENOMENA IN ELECTRICAL POWER SYSTEMS

by

V. A. VENIKOV

Abridged translation by

BERNARD ADKINS

M.A., D.Sc., M.I.E.E.

and

DANIEL RUTENBERG

B.Sc., A.M.I.E.E.

A Pergamon Press Book

THE MACMILLAN COMPANY

NEW YORK

1964

THE MACMILLAN COMPANY
60 Fifth Avenue
New York 11, N. Y.

This book is distributed by
THE MACMILLAN COMPANY
pursuant to a special arrangement with
PERGAMON PRESS LIMITED
Oxford, England

This translation has been made from the original Russian volume
Elektromekhanicheskiye perekhodnyye protsessy v elektricheskikh sistemakh,
published in 1958 by Gosenergoizdat, Moscow–Leningrad,

Library of Congress Catalog Card Number: 62–8706

PRINTED IN POLAND
PWN—DUAM

CONTENTS

71565

viii   *Contents*

CHAPTER 5. METHODS OF IMPROVING THE POWER-HANDLING CAPACITY AND
STABILITY OF TRANSMISSION LINES AND POWER SYSTEMS

AUTHOR'S PREFACE
TO THE ENGLISH EDITION

THE English version of my book is an abridgement of the original Russian work. The abridgement, undertaken by the translators, Dr. B. Adkins and Mr. D. Rutenberg, with the consent of the author, presents to the reader a number of topics which have so far received relatively little attention in English technical literature. It is likely that the continuity of the book has suffered somewhat by this process of selection, but the author hopes nevertheless that the English reader will benefit from the efforts of the translators to choose the material of special interest to him.

The Russian version of the book is based on the course of lectures given by the author over a period of 20 years to undergraduate and postgraduate students of the Moscow Power Institute.

The material presented in the book is treated in a somewhat different manner from that adopted in other books on the same subject, published both in the Soviet Union and abroad. In the author's opinion the problems associated with transient phenomena in power systems are closely linked with their automatic control, and in the present work an attempt has been made to bring out this intrinsic connexion.

The transient phenomena are classified under three headings:
- (a) Those associated with small changes of power and small changes of speed.
- (b) Those associated with large changes of power and small changes of speed.
- (c) Those associated with large changes of power and large changes of speed.

Much attention is given in the book to the so-called forced excitation of power systems, which has already found practical application in the Soviet Union in the Kuibyshev and Volgograd hydro-electric stations. There is little doubt that this type of control, when extended to the prime movers (speed and frequency regulation), will find wide application not only for long-distance transmission but also in closely interconnected networks of the type used in Great Britain.

The methods given in the book for calculating the stability and the transient behaviour of systems with forced excitation control have several

novel features. In particular, methods developed in the U.S.S.R. for studying steady-state stability include the method of small oscillations and
the method of domain separation.

The author hopes that his book will be of interest to his British col-
leagues. He will feel especially happy if it also contributes to the strengthen-
ing of scientific and cultural ties and the development of friendly relations between the engineers and scientists of Great Britain and of the
Soviet Union.

V. A. VENIKOV
Professor, Moscow Power Institute
Doctor of Technical Sciences

TRANSLATORS' PREFACE

The present volume is an abridged translation of an important Russian book by Professor V. A. Venikov, who is a well-known authority in the field of Power Systems Analysis. During 1952, 1956, 1958 and 1960, he made important contributions to the C.I.G.R.E. Conference in Paris and to the British Association meetings in Cardiff. It is hoped that this English version of his book will help readers in Western countries to become acquainted with some of the new developments which have taken place in the Soviet Union.

Professor Venikov's book, which deals with transient phenomena in electrical power systems, is a comprehensive text-book intended for students at the Moscow Power Institute. It is a very long book, including much material with which English readers are familiar, but it also contains many new ideas and methods of calculation which are of very great interest at the present time. The abridged translation, which is about a third of the length of the original work, gives a selection from the parts relating to the new material.

The Russian book is divided into four parts:

    I Introduction.

    II Theoretical basis.

    III Calculations.

    IV Applications.

Of this material the Introduction has been translated in full, while Part II, occupying about one-half of the original work, accounts for two-thirds of the translation. The principal topics treated are the analysis of new methods of regulating the excitation of alternators, and of dealing with fault conditions which cause the machines to lose synchronism. The analysis of stability by the method of small oscillations is given a good deal of attention. On the other hand, sections dealing with the equal-area criterion, step-by-step methods and other familiar topics, have been omitted in the translation. Several sections which give a detailed analysis of complicated systems have also been left out.

Part III *Calculations* and Part IV *Applications* are represented in the translation by the sections giving summaries of the methods, since the detailed discussion in the original is mainly an extension of the material treated in Part II.

The abridged version is as far as possible an exact translation of the selected sections of the Russian book, and only occasionally have a few sentences been inserted for the sake of continuity.

Imperial College,
London,
June 1963

B. ADKINS
D. RUTENBERG

PRINCIPAL SYMBOLS

a regulation coefficient

a_P, a_Q active, reactive load regulation coefficient

$a_{1,2}$ relative acceleration

E electro-motive force

E_d synchronous e. m. f. (proportional to field current)

E' transient e. m. f. (proportional to field flux)

E_d' direct-axis transient e. m. f.

E_x voltage behind effective reactance Δx

f frequency

I, i current

I_d direct axis current

I_q quadrature oxis current

J inertia coefficient

k gain coefficient

P active power

P_s, P_{as} synchronous, asynchronous components of active power

P_t turbine power

P_d damping coefficient

Q reactive power

Q_μ magnetizing component of reactive power

Q_s component of reactive power depending on leakage

Q_s, Q_{as} synchronous, asynchronous components of reactive power

R, r resistance

S complex power

S_{E_d} synchronizing power coefficient, steady

S_{E_d}' synchronizing power coefficient, transient

s slip

T torque

T_t turbine torque

T_s, T_{as} synchronous, asynchronous components of torque

V voltage

V_g generator terminal voltage

$W_u(p)$ transfer function of regulator

X, x reactance

x_d direct-axis synchronous reactance

x_q quadrature-axis synchronous reactance

x_d' direct axis transient reactance

x_d'' direct axis sub-transient reactance

x_q'' quadrature-axis sub-transient reactance

x_s reactance of external system

x_μ magnetizing reactance

x_{dt}, x_{dt}' total reactance of a circuit

Y, y admittance

$\alpha_{1,2}$ transfer impedance angle

δ load angle

μ turbine valve movement

τ time constant

τ_d' direct-axis transient time constant

τ_d'' direct-axis sub-transient time constant

τ_q'' quadrature-axis sub-transient time constant

τ_e exciter time constant

τ_r regulator time constant

ω angular frequency

Ω turbine speed

INTRODUCTION

General Aspects of the Subject

This book deals with the study of transient phenomena in electrical power systems. An electrical system consists of many separate elements combined together. There are, first, the *power elements*, which generate, transform, transmit, distribute, and consume the electrical energy, and secondly *control elements*, which automatically regulate the conditions in the system.

When the system is operating, all the elements interact with each other; at any given time they form the system which acts as a unit for the purpose of producing, transmitting, distributing and consuming electrical energy.

In order to control these processes, it is necessary to study not only the electrical action of the power elements of the system, but also their mechanical action. Such effects occur in the prime movers (turbines), the mechanical energy of which is transformed by the generators into electrical energy, and in the motors forming the load of the electrical system, where electrical energy is transformed into mechanical energy. It must always be kept in mind that, when separate elements are combined to form a system, they can gain new properties and that there is an essential difference between the functioning of the system as a whole, and that of its separate elements.

Thus the book deals with the analysis of transient phenomena in electro-mechanical systems, and of the steady conditions which precede or follow a transient condition.

In the normal operation of a power system, the most important quantity is the power produced in the generators and transmitted to the consumers. The "quality" of the energy produced is defined by the magnitude of the voltage at the consumers' terminals and by the frequency established in the system. For a more complete description it is also important to know the voltages at various nodal points and the currents flowing through the elements of the system.

The condition of a system, described by the above quantities, is defined as its *state*. Several kinds of state of an electrical system can be distinguished. The *normal steady state* is that for which the system is designed and is most important from the economic point of view. A *steady fault condition* arises after the disconnexion, due to a fault, of one or more elements of the system. In these circumstances, the system is likely to have inferior characteristics compared with its normal steady state.

The power, the voltage, the current, the frequency, and the degree of stability, which indicate the condition of operation of the system, may be called the *variables defining the state*. The impedances, the admittances, the transformation ratios, etc., which indicate the characteristics of the elements, are called the parameters of the elements of the system, or, more briefly, the *system parameters*.

A *transient state* occurs when the system is changing from one steady state to another. A distinction is made between a *normal transient* (occurring during normal operation) and a *fault transient*. Since the conditions in the system during a transient state are continually changing, it is more appropriate and convenient in practice to consider separate *transient processes*, which, in combination, make up the overall transient state. Here again, there is the distinction between normal and fault transients.

A *normal transient process* occurs during ordinary operation. It is caused by the connexion or disconnexion of a transformer or a transmission line, or by any other ordinary switching operation, which brings in or removes a generator or a load or changes the amount of power. During a normal transient, the variables defining the state do not usually differ greatly from their values in the normal steady state, and the condition is referred to as a *small disturbance*. A succession of small disturbances, for example, changes of load, occurs continually, so that, strictly speaking, the system never operates in a steady state. A so-called steady state is, in reality, one which is subject to small disturbances such that the variables defining the state fluctuate between different steady values. The normal transients are initiated by the personnel operating the system or by automatic devices, and the changes are such that there are no sharp discontinuities in the values of the variables.

A *fault transient process*, on the other hand, is caused by some accidental change in the system. The circuit of the system may suddenly alter, changing the conditions drastically; for example, heavily loaded generators or transmission lines may be disconnected or a short circuit may occur on a transmission line or elsewhere, followed by the disconnexion of a part of the system. During a fault transient there are sharp discontinuities in the values of the variables.

The changes in the circuit connexions, normally brought about by automatic switchgear actuated by protective relays, may sometimes cause such radical changes in the conditions that the system is quite unable to operate satisfactorily after the fault. Such a result constitutes a complete breakdown of the system. If, on the other hand, the values of the variables after the fault do not differ greatly from those in normal operation, the system has been able to withstand satisfactorily the shock caused by the fault.

In order to control the operation of a system correctly so as to prevent breakdowns and to design suitable protective and automatic control gear, the engineer must have a clear and detailed picture of all the possible phenomena in a modern power system. He must foresee what will happen to the system as a result of this or that change in its operation. Only then can he determine the required parameters of the equipment and of the protective and automatic gear in order to obtain the best results from the system as a whole and from its constituent parts.

The duration of a transient condition in any system is usually incomparably shorter than that of the normal steady condition. Nevertheless, the overall merit of an electrical system is to a great extent determined by its transient behaviour. A system which lacks stability in a transient state has as little practical value as, for example, an aeroplane which is unstable during take-off or landing, even though it performs well when flying at constant speed.

The present study of transient phenomena in electrical systems discusses in the first place the *short-period transient processes* associated with changes in the electro-mechanical condition of the system. The study of these phenomena is not carried out for its own sake but because it provides an essential aid in understanding the methods used to ensure that the system can withstand the shock due to any fault, and can operate stably when subjected to any normal small disturbances. It is thus necessary to study not only the transient conditions, but also the normal steady state and the steady fault condition, since these can often be taken as the initial and final states of the system.

The book deals with electromagnetic and electro-mechanical phenomena, taking into account the mutual action between the components of the system. The behaviour of a system, when all of its elements from the prime mover to the load are subject to change, is discussed. Considerable attention is given to the problem of determining the conditions required for stability.

The question of stability is important not only in electrical power systems, but arises also in the study of any engineering structure, for example, a bridge, an automatic pilot for a ship or an aeroplane, or a radar device. Although these structures differ greatly in their physical nature, they have much in common in the matter of stability. The classical paper entitled *The general problem of dynamic stability*, published in 1892 by the great Russian mathematician A. M. Lyapunov, serves as a basis for any investigation of stability problems.

Before proceeding with the detailed discussion of stability, it is appropriate to emphasize that the electrical power system is a most important part of the general economic structure of any industrialized country. A power system may consist of a large number of stations each giving a very large output. In the Soviet Union at the present time there are over 50 separate power systems, many of which have an annual output in excess of 10^9 kWh and several of which have more than 1200 km of transmission lines. The latest addition is the transmission line from Kuibyshev, which is 1000 km long and is designed to deliver more than 6×10^9 kWh annually. This line, and those from the Volgograd station and the Siberian superstations on the rivers Angara, Ob and Yenissei, will be powerful links in a single high-voltage super-grid.

A power system, which may contain different types of station, hydraulic or thermal, must operate in a stable manner. The variables defining the state of the system—its frequency, its power output, the voltage supplied to the consumers—must be maintained within certain limits.

From the technical and economic point of view a complex power system containing a number of interconnected stations has many advantages. There are, however, some special difficulties in the operation of such a system. Thus, a fault which disturbs the stability of the system affects the whole system and not only the part in which the fault occurs. The larger and more complex the system, the more serious is the consequence of a fault, particularly if the engineer is unable to design the system correctly and does not understand clearly the nature of the transient conditions which may arise. If a complex power system is not correctly designed, or is not correctly operated, the after-effects of a fault may be catastrophic.

Theoretical and practical investigations made by Soviet scientists and engineers—S. A. Lebedev, P. S. Zhdanov, A. A. Gorev, I. A. Syromyatnikov and many others, including the operating staff of the various systems, have made it possible to improve the stability of power systems to such an extent, that accidents leading to instability are now extremely rare.

Not so very long ago (between 1929 and 1935) there were 44 faults leading to instability in one of our largest power systems. These break-downs were responsible for 70 per cent of the loss of supply to the consumers. Such figures bring out very clearly the value of the theoretical and practical work, which has now made it possible to eliminate this kind of breakdown almost completely. It is clear that, with the further development of power systems, it becomes even more important to study the transient phenomena and the means for their control.

The operational experience gained on the Ural Power System may serve as an example of what can be achieved by applying the theory in practice. In 1943, when the system was very fully loaded, there were 33 faults causing loss of stability. After introducing better operational techniques, including automatic control of the generators and other equipment, the number of breakdowns was reduced to only two in 1944, and none in 1945.

While, however, there is no great difficulty in applying these methods to the smaller systems, the problems arising in systems with very long transmission lines are not yet fully understood. So far we have no criterion which guarantees optimum stability conditions when the system is heavily loaded.

The planning of a unified high-voltage super-grid for the whole of the Soviet Union has brought to the fore the problem of designing and operating long transmission lines. It is essential to increase their power-handling capacity while maintaining stability. These transmission links present special stability problems, which are being actively studied at the present time. This book discusses the methods used for ensuring stable operation and the lines of possible future development. A much fuller treatment of the subject will be given by the author in a later book entitled *Special problems in electrical power systems.*

The study of transient phenomena in electrical power systems is now of especial importance because of the increasing use of electronic rectifying devices for automatic and remote control.

The operation of a power system under automatic control consists of a continuous sequence of transient effects, caused by the action of the automatic devices, and by the reaction of the system on them. Thus an understanding of the nature of the transients is essential for the correct assessment of the operation of the automatic regulators, and of their design, adjustment and application under normal working conditions. The distinction between transient and steady states tends to disappear under these conditions. The automatic devices are evidently important elements in determining the transient behaviour of the system. The present book does not discuss the design, nor the theory of operation, of the devices themselves. They are treated merely as elements which affect other elements so as to bring about changes in the operation of the system.

In general, the properties of the elements of the system are dealt with elsewhere. The present book is concerned with the complex phenomena arising in systems as a whole, and particularly with the new properties acquired by such systems, as a result of the combining together of the separate elements. It is intended to serve as a basis for a more detailed study of the subject. The object is to give an understanding of the physical phenomena which occur, to set out the principles underlying the methods of calculation, and to indicate the means used to control the operation of the system.

General Classification of Transient Phenomena

Generally speaking, a transient condition occurs in a system whenever it is undergoing a change from one state to another. During the transient change, there is a change of the amount of energy in the electrical or electro-mechanical parts of the system. A transient condition may be studied in relation to both space and time, or if it is permissible to assume that the change of any quantity occurs simultaneously at every point in the space considered, in time only. In the first case, the parameters are distributed and, in the second, they are lumped. Conditions, for which the quantities must be considered in space as well as in time, include those where the distribution of potential is required in long transmission lines or cables, or in the windings of machines or transformers.

The duration of the phenomena discussed in this book is generally considerably in excess of the time of propagation in space of the physical quantities (such as current or voltage) in terms of which they are expressed. It is therefore permissible to consider them as happening in circuits containing lumped parameters. Consequently the book does not discuss wave propagation, and is not concerned with the inner construction of the elements to which the lumped parameters refer.

It is important to note, however, that this restricted point of view may become inadequate in the very near future. The use of exciters with automatic control, whose action is dependent on the changes of the first and second derivatives of the quantities being controlled, may make it neccessary to allow for wave propagation in a long transmission line simultaneously with the electro-mechanical phenomena. Similarly, when high-speed regulators are used with water turbines, it may be necessary to allow for wave propagation in the pipe line. It appears likely that, in the future, it may be necessary to study electro-mechanical systems with distributed parameters in order to obtain exact solutions of certain problems. At the moment, however, there is no need to do so in practical work. Moreover, many of the problems are not yet fully solved and so are not included in the present treatment.

Transient phenomena can be classified into three types:

1. *Wave propagation phenomena.* The effect of transient voltages due to switching, lightning strokes, or other causes, depends on the "wave" parameters of the system. A change in the mechanical conditions, such as a variation of the speed of a generator or a turbine, has no effect on this type of transient process.

2. *Electromagnetic phenomena.* The electromagnetic action is assumed to be unaffected by the mechanical state of the system in which it occurs. For this type of condition the generators are assumed to run at constant speed.

3. *Electro-mechanical phenomena.* The variations of speed of the generators, the turbines, and the motor loads, have a decisive influence on the behaviour. The electromagnetic and electro-mechanical effects must be considered together. The main purpose of the present book is to study transient phenomena of this type.

Any transient phenomenon may be studied either by assuming linearity for all the circuit parameters or, alternatively, by allowing for non-linearity, which is always present to some extent, since any process which modifies the physical state of the medium in which it occurs must affect the parameters. In many cases, however, the effect may be either wholly or partially neglected.

The solution of any transient problem can therefore be carried out either by a linear method or by a non-linear method. There is an essential difference between the two methods.

A system is defined to be linear in a physical sense, if the nature of any change taking place in it is independent of its magnitude. In a linear system a change due to two or more independent disturbances can be determined as the sum of the changes, caused by each of the disturbances acting separately.

There is another important aspect of the methods of investigation considered here, since most of them are concerned with alternating voltages at 50 c/s. On the one hand the transient condition may be considered from the point of view of the instantaneous changes of current and voltage, and studied by means of equations relating the instantaneous values. On the other hand, a more general approach may be made by disregarding the instantaneous values and considering only the envelopes of the curves (Fig. 1). Electro-mechanical processes in electrical systems are associated with the displacement of heavy rotors and the change of stored magnetic energy in large generators, and take place so slowly that it is permissible

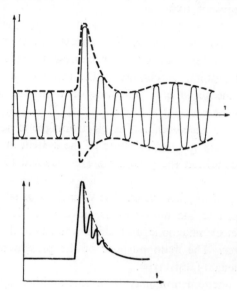

Fig. 1. Instantaneous values of currents *I* and *i* (full lines) and their envelopes.

to regard the 50 c/s sinusoidal variations as "micro-processes" and consider only the changes in the envelopes.

This approach is inadmissible, however, for the study of wave propagation and other rapid electromagnetic phenomena, since the time rate of change is then comparable with that of the sinusoidal voltage.

It is worth noting that any change of state of an electrical system is accompanied by many other different effects. For example, a short circuit causes large currents to flow in the generators and the rest of the system. The currents produce heat in the conductors, and the various parts of the system are subjected to mechanical forces, which may sometimes cause serious damage. Sudden changes of current, of voltage, or of stored electromagnetic energy in the system may set up electromagnetic radiation, and so on. It is obviously very difficult to study such a complicated process in full detail, and there is no need to do so in practice. The engineer must strive to simplify the problem, by separating out the effects which are important for the solution of a given practical problem.

The effects may be separated out in this way in most engineering problems, and, with the aid of appropriate theoretical and practical methods, can be expressed in terms of relatively few variables. Such an approach clarifies the general nature of the phenomenon, and though leaving out a good deal of detail, nevertheless gives a reliable statement of the problem.

The simplifications introduced in the treatment given in this book are also important because they clarify the concepts which underlie the operation of the system and of its elements and make it easier to understand and verify the calculations. An engineer must base his work not only on a sound theory but also on a clear physical picture of the conditions he is studying. He must know how to set out his results simply and clearly, using simplified circuits and models where necessary. For this reason the treatment of many questions in this book is not mathematically rigorous, but ignores the effect of secondary factors, thus simplifying the solution. It is true that the increasing complexity of modern power systems often makes it necessary to use more refined methods of analysis of the automatic control systems, and hence, more advanced mathematical and physical methods. Their use is, however, only justified when a simpler solution is either inadequate or even quite inadmissible.

The method of presentation adopted in this book therefore starts with a discussion of a number of simplified physical concepts and later develops them in greater depth by means of appropriate mathematical methods.

The use of equivalent circuits or idealized components appears to be particularly suitable for the study of transient phenomena, because they help to bring out the essential features of the problem. For example, a long transmission line, in which complicated wave propagation effects occur, can usually, when electro-mechanical problems have to be solved, be treated as a simplified equivalent network containing lumped impedances and capacitances. Many problems can be further simplified by neglecting resistance and representing the line as a pure reactance. For many calculations and investigations the generators may be represented by the reactances x_d, x_q or x'_d, and the corresponding voltages behind these reactances. Strictly, the equivalent circuit of the generator, unlike that of the line, must vary under transient conditions, and the values of the reactances and the voltages behind them must be functions of time. It is, however, often possible to simplify the problem by neglecting the variations, and assuming the reactances and the voltages to be constant over a limited period of time.

As already mentioned, the book deals with electro-mechanical processes.

Consequently the treatment is based on the laws of mechanics as well as on the laws of electromagnetism.

From the point of view of modern mechanics and of the theory of oscillations, it is frequently possible to treat an electro-mechanical system as a "displacement system", i.e. a system whose state depends on the relative position of its elements, but not on the velocity with which the elements move to any position. For the purpose of studying the steady-state stability of a power system, its electrical part can be considered to be such a displacement system, in which it can be assumed that the power produced in the generators, or consumed in the loads, depends only on the phase and magnitude of the generator voltages, and on the values of impedance used to represent the generators and loads.

In a displacement system the power developed by the generators, the stability and other properties, do not depend on the absolute speeds of the generators, nor of the motors constituting the load, and there is no need to consider the changes in the system variables due to changes of frequency. The problem becomes unduly complex if the frequency characteristic of the system is taken into account.

For a study of mechanical oscillations a system can often be considered to be a "conservative system", i.e. one without losses, in which the sum of the kinetic and potential energies (the total energy) at any instant is constant, even though its parts move relatively to one another.

Most of the problems discussed in this book relate specifically to conservative systems. This means that, for most practical purposes, the losses due to friction, and the losses associated with damping torques caused by relative movement of the rotor, are neglected.

More complicated problems, which are only considered qualitatively in the book, are met in the study of "dissipative systems", in which there are forces opposing the motion which depend on the changes of speed. In dissipative systems there are energy losses, so that the total energy of the system does not remain constant when its parts are in relative motion.

Electrical systems containing rotating machines are "oscillatory systems", i.e. the rotors of the machines may, under certain conditions, oscillate about an equilibrium position. When control devices are used they may become "self-oscillating systems", in which sustained or increasing oscillations occur. The self-oscillation may be caused by an external source of energy which replenishes the store of internal energy in the system. Thus a valve which controls the supply of energy to the oscillating system may be associated with a feed-back loop, through which the system reacts on the valve.

The ordinary pendulum is an example of an oscillating system. A simple example of a self-oscillating system is the frictional pendulum shown in Fig. 2. When energy enters the system from outside, due to a periodic

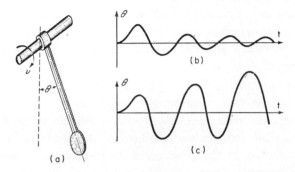

FIG. 2. Frictional pendulum an example of a self-oscillating system. (*a*) sketch of the pendulum; (*b*) damped oscillation; shaft stationary ($v = 0$); (*c*) self-oscillation with increasing amplitude, shaft rotating ($v \neq 0$).

change of one of its parameters, the self-oscillating system is described as a "parametric system". An example of such a system is a swing, of the type shown in Fig. 3, in which a man standing on the swing can set up an oscillation of increasing amplitude by bending and straightening

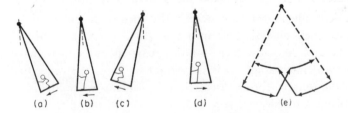

FIG. 3. A swing, an example of a parametric system. To maintain oscillation the operator bends his body at the end points of the movement (*a*) and (*c*), and straightens it suddenly while passing through the mid-position (*b*) and (*d*); (*e*) the displacement of the centre of gravity of the operator.

his body, thus changing the position of the centre of gravity of the pendulum, and thereby introducing additional energy by a periodic change of a parameter.

When dealing with transient phenomena in different types of system — mechanical, electrical and electro-mechanical—it is essential to introduce the concept of "generalized coordinates" and of the "number of degrees of freedom" of the given system. The generalized coordinates are the physical quantities, defined above as the variables of the system, which vary with changing conditions. The generalized coordinates describe the transient condition existing during such a change. The number of degrees of freedom of the system is equal to the number of independent variables required to provide a reasonably complete statement of the condition being considered.

For a determination of the voltages and currents under transient conditions in a complicated electrical network, containing resistances and inductive and capacitative reactances, the number of degrees of freedom is equal to the number of independent meshes in the network. If the mesh currents are chosen as the generalized coordinates, these are the actual currents in the branches forming the boundary of the network. In any other branch the current is equal to the difference between two adjacent mesh currents, if the positive sense of all the mesh currents is taken in the same direction. The number of mesh currents n_i is given by the difference between the number of independent meshes n_m and the number of current sources n_e.

If the system is capable of motion, and every mesh moves independently, the number of degrees of freedom increases. An electrical machine has one mechanical degree of freedom, and the number of independent coordinates required to describe the system is therefore (n_i+1).

Transient phenomena are defined by means of differential equations and hence their analysis falls into two parts—first, the setting up of the equations, and secondly, their solution, carried out either analytically or by numerical integration. It is important to know the order of the equations at the outset; for electrical circuit problems when the instantaneous values of the variables are required, the order of the differential equations may be determined by a method due to D. A. Gorodskoy. Any inductances or capacitances connected in series in a given branch are considered as one unit when determining the total number (n_L+n_C) of inductances L and capacitances C. The order of the differential equations is then equal to this number, decreased by the number of independent nodes n_n joining the branches containing both inductance and capacitance, and further decreased by the number n_m of independent meshes containing only capacitance or only inductance. The rule can be expressed mathematically as

$$n = (n_L+n_C)-n_n-n_m .$$

To determine the order of the equation describing a transient process in a complicated electro-mechanical system the formula suggested by L. V. Zukernik may be used. This formula takes account of the relative position of the machine rotors but treats the electromagnetic phenomena in a simplified manner by neglecting the asymmetrical components and by considering the envelopes rather than the instantaneous values.

$$n = 2\Sigma M + \Sigma\tau + \Sigma a_\omega - (1-a_\sim)(1-a_\delta)\left[1+(1-a_\approx)(1-a_D)\right]$$

where

ΣM — the number of synchronous and asynchronous machines, whose mechanical action is included;

$\Sigma\tau$ — the number of time constants allowing for electromagnetic inertia in the exciting circuits of the synchronous machines;

Σa_ω — the number of static loads for which the variation of impedance with frequency is considered;

$a_\sim$ = 1 for a system with bus-bars of constant voltage and frequency;

$a_\sim$ = 0 when there are no such bus-bars;

a_δ = 1 for synchronous machines with excitation control depending on the load angle (rather than on derivatives of the angle);

a_δ = 0 when there are no such machines;

$a_\approx$ = 1 for induction motor and static loads, for which the variation of impedance with frequency is considered. In this case $\Sigma a_\omega \neq 0$ and mechanical inertia effects of asynchronous machines are not neglected;

$a_\approx$ = 0 when there are no such loads;

a_D = 1 for synchronous machines (even a single machine) for which mechanical damping is considered;

a_D = 0 when such effects are neglected.

If the system contains a group of ideally similar machines (i.e. machines having the same parameters, the same excitation and regulator system, and the same connexions between machines), such a group can be treated in this calculation as a single equivalent machine.

In applying this method the instantaneous values of the variables are not determined, so that the number of inductances and capacitances involved is immaterial, the time constants of the respective branches being used instead.

The foregoing discussion may be summarized as follows. Electrical systems, considered from the point of view of their electro-mechanical operation, are very complicated. They are self-exciting non-linear systems and may act as parametric systems. They have characteristics depending on frequency and are dissipative systems. The number of degrees of freedom is very great and their behaviour is expressed by differential equations of a high order. As a rule the transient phenomena in a system cannot be considered in full detail, and in an engineering solution it is only possible to study the separate processes.

In order to give a clearer exposition of the subject, the material is classified, somewhat arbitrarily, under three main headings:

1. Under the first heading are considered conditions where large variations of power, current and voltage are associated with small variations of generator speed. The problems considered include transient stability, correct synchronization, swinging of the generator rotor, methods of forced excitation, etc.

2. The second heading covers conditions due to small disturbances (small changes) in the system, and small deviations of the rotors from their mean positions. It is an important point that the small variations of power, current and voltage are accompanied by only slight variations of generator speed. The following problems are discussed under this heading: steady-state stability, small swings in a machine connected to a system, the operation of automatic control devices under normal conditions, the adjustment of such devices for optimum performance, and criteria for their stability when operating in the system. These matters are treated by assuming linear conditions. The differential equations are linearized by considering only small variations, and they are analysed by finding the roots of the characteristic equation.

3. Under the third heading are considered the problems in which large variations of power are associated with large variations of speed. These problems include the starting and acceleration of generating sets, asynchronous operation of synchronous generators when connected to the system, resynchronization, self-synchronization, and unsynchronized automatic reclosing of the switches.

It is evident that the above classification is an artificial one. The methods of one section can often be applied satisfactorily to the problems considered under a different heading. Nevertheless, from a general point of view, the arrangement adopted appears to be justifiable for the purpose of obtaining an easy method of solving practical problems.

CHAPTER 1

CHARACTERISTICS OF THE COMPONENTS
OF AN ELECTRICAL SYSTEM

1.1. Excitation Systems for Synchronous Generators and Condensers

The principal requirements in an excitation system are quick response and high sensitivity. This can be attained if the exciter has a high ceiling voltage, which makes it possible to operate for a limited period with a voltage 4 to 5 times greater than normal. The higher the ceiling voltage the faster is the rise of the current, as shown by the relation

$$i = i_{e \cdot \text{nom}}(1 - \varepsilon^{-t/\tau_e}).$$

The rate of rise of the voltage should be very rapid, say, 2000–3000 V/sec.

The exciting system must also be able to produce a rapid fall of voltage by demagnetizing the field when a fault occurs.

The power to operate an excitation system should be kept low and the system should be able to operate with any kind of regulator. Since the excitation system plays a most important part in the operation of a generator set, it must have a high *degree of reliability* consistent with simplicity and it must be suitable for fully automatic control.

These requirements are particularly important for generators feeding long transmission lines. They cannot be easily met by the ordinary methods of excitation and hence special systems have been designed for the large generators in main power stations. The special systems must also be able to supply the considerable amount of power required for their excitation.

As an example, some particulars of the exciters used in the Kuibyshev station may be quoted. The nominal operating voltage of the exciter is 380 V, the nominal exciter current is about 2000 A, and the ceiling voltage is about 1600 V. When forcing is used the rate of rise of the voltage is 2000 V/sec. Two systems for meeting such requirements have recently been developed, one with quick response rotating machines and the other with electronic devices.

The excitation system using quick response machines, shown in Fig. 1.1, was specially developed for the Kuibyshev hydro-electric station.

The main exciter is direct-coupled to the generator and is connected in series with a booster. The booster has two field windings supplied by the control devices, one designed for continuous operation at − 800 V and the other for intermittent operation at + 800 V. Under normal operating conditions the booster supplies about − 400 V, which, combined with the main exciter voltage, gives a voltage across the field winding of the alternator of about + 400 V. When forcing is used the booster voltage is changed instantaneously by the control devices from − 400 V to + 800 V, thus applying to the alternator field a ceiling voltage four times greater than normal, i.e. 1600 V. The time constant of the booster field winding is reduced to 0·1–0·2 sec by introducing additional resistance.

In this scheme (Fig. 1.1) particular attention has been paid to the reliability of the high-speed booster 2 under conditions of forced excitation.

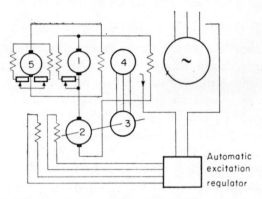

Fig. 1.1. Excitation system for the alternators of the Kuibyshev hydro-electric station, using quick response machines. (1) main exciter, 1600 kW, 800 V, 2000 A, 68·2 r.p.m.; (2) booster, 900 kW, ± 800 V, 2000 A, 745 r.p.m.; (3) induction motor for booster 900 kW, 3000 V, 745 r.p.m.; (4) auxiliary generator, 3125 kVA (2500 kW), 3150 V, 68·2 r.p.m.; (5) exciter of auxiliary generator 84 kW, 210 V, 68·2 r.p.m.

This is achieved by providing a suitable overload capacity of the induction motor 3 and by using a large auxiliary generator 4.

An electronic excitation system intended for a similar alternator is shown in Fig. 1.2. The stator winding of the auxiliary generator 2 is designed to give a voltage of about 1400 V, with a tap at 460 V. The system has two rectifiers, one (2R) operating at full voltage and the other (1R) at 460 V. The main control equipment and the rectifier equipment are housed in two racks (1C and 2C). The rectifiers are supplied from a separate transformer 4. The auxiliary generator has a normal exciter 3, which can be forced up to 2½ times its normal voltage when forced excitation is applied to the main alternator. The rectified voltage is applied to the field winding of the main alternator 1.

The magnitude of the rectified voltage is controlled by controlling the firing angle of the rectifier.[1] In the circuit shown in Fig. 1.2,

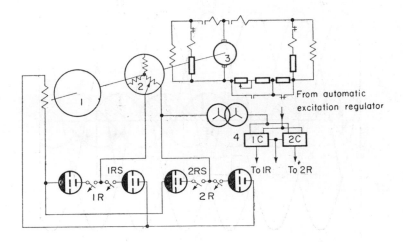

FIG. 1.2. Electronic exciter for a large hydro-electric alternator. (1) main alternator; (2) auxiliary generator, 2500 kW; (3) exciter of auxiliary generator; (4) auxiliary transformer for electronic exciter. 1R, 2R, rectifiers; 1C, 2C rectifier control racks; 1RS, 2RS, quick-action anode switches.

the grids of the valves are connected to a negative blocking voltage of −100 V, which is modulated as required by a pulse of +250 V to make the valves conducting. In the grid control scheme developed by *Ural-electroapparat*, the positive pulses are produced in special peak generators. The magnitude of the rectified voltage is controlled by the change of the phase angle between the anode voltage and the input voltage to the peak generator, using a combination of rotary and static phase shifters.

The three-phase bridge circuit used for the Kuibyshev generators consists of two three-phase rectifiers connected in series and displaced by 60° relative to each other. The rectified voltage is then equal to the sum of the voltages of the two three-phase rectifiers.

A detailed description of the operation of a complicated excitation system with two groups of valves, as shown in Fig. 1.2, is outside the scope of the present book. Figure 1.3 gives some curves of rectified voltage for different conditions of operation, allowing for the commutation of the current. The mean value of the rectified voltage is given by the area under the voltage curve, taken over a complete period.

During normal operation of the generator between no load and maximum load, the voltage supplied by the electronic exciter to the field

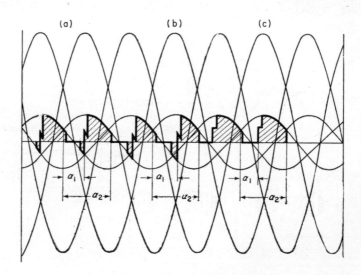

FIG. 1.3. Operational characteristics of an electronic exciter. Rectified voltage due to two groups of valves. (*a*) normal load of alternator; (*b*) alternator open-circuited; (*c*) maximum load of alternator.

winding through the slip-rings is varied by changing the phase of the input voltage of the peak generator which controls the grid voltage of the rectifier valves. Hand control is obtained by means of a rotary phase shifter. The grid voltages of the low-voltage valves are remote-controlled by a servo motor, while those for the high-voltage valves are controlled by hand. The rotary phase shifters allow a phase shift of 120°.

Static phase shifters are used for automatic control by the excitation regulator. They are connected in the grid circuit between the rotary phase shifter and the peak generator. Figure 1.4(*a*) is a key diagram for one phase of a three-phase static phase shifter. As indicated in the diagram, the circuit forms a bridge, two arms of which are the secondary windings of a transformer fed from the rotary phase shifter, while the third arm is a fixed resistance and the fourth a variable inductance. The inductance is varied by means of an auxiliary winding on the iron core, which is fed from the automatic excitation regulator. Variation of the direct current in the auxiliary winding changes the value of the inductance and varies the phase of the voltage V_b across the diagonal of the bridge without altering its magnitude (Fig. 1.4(*b*)).

Under certain fault conditions it is necessary to demagnetize the generator field. This is accomplished by blocking the low-voltage rectifiers

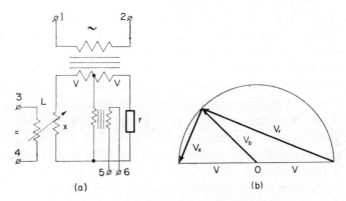

FIG. 1.4. Single-phase static phase-shifter: (*a*) basic circuit; (*b*) voltage vector diagram. *r*—fixed non-reactive resistor; *L*—variable reactor controlled by automatic excitation regulator via terminals 3 and 4; 1,2, terminals fed from manually controlled phase-shifter; 5, 6, terminals fed from peak-generator.

and transferring the whole of the load to the high-voltage valves, which then act as inverters. The voltage across the generator field winding becomes negative and the field decays very rapidly. On the other hand, if forcing is required, the regulation angle of the high-voltage valves is reduced to zero, causing them to take over the whole load and to provide a higher mean rectifier voltage.

Automatic control of excitation

Until recently it has been accepted that the main function of an automatic excitation regulator, was to maintain during normal operation a specified voltage across the station bus-bars and the supply network. Now, however, the function of excitation control has broadened considerably. Control of the excitation under fault conditions or immediately after a fault has made it possible to improve the stability of stations operating in parallel, to stabilize the load, to prevent a sudden fall of voltage and to ensure satisfactory starting of induction motors. With suitable automatic control it is practicable to operate single generators or even whole stations asynchronously. With forced excitation the reliability of protective devices is increased, and, due to the reduced values of the voltages occurring after a fault, the system returns to normal operation more rapidly.

Hence, while the terms "voltage regulator" and "excitation regulator" are virtually synonymous, the term "automatic excitation regulator", abbreviated to AER, will be used henceforth.

Investigations of new methods of automatic control of excitation have shown its importance in improving the steady-state stability of long transmission lines. They have also shown the desirability of designing excitation regulators which respond, not only to changes of voltage, but also to changes of other quantities, such as current, load angle δ, etc.

The automatic devices used for excitation control are so intimately connected with the whole excitation system that it is not correct to consider them in isolation, and they must be considered as a unit, having certain properties and operating characteristics, and satisfying definite requirements. The main requirements to be satisfied by the automatic devices, used to control the excitation of synchronous machines, are that they shall increase the steady-state and transient stability and maintain constant voltage, both under normal conditions and, often under fault conditions when a forced increase of reactive power is required. These requirements need not be satisfied by a single regulating device but may be met by a combination of several machines and other apparatus, which form a so-called *automatic control system* (abbreviated to ACS).

The requirements which should be satisfied by such a system can be formulated as follows:

(*a*) For a generator connected to a long line, the ACS should ensure that the operational capacity of the line can be utilized up to its limit. The condition may be one of "artificial stability", by which is understood an operating condition of an alternator, which can only be maintained with the aid of automatic control. If the automatic control fails the alternator goes out of synchronism.

(*b*) The control system should provide a good margin of transient stability and should help to damp down the hunting of the alternator rotor after a fault.

(*c*) The stability of operation must be maintained when changes occur in the parameters of the system to which the alternator is connected. Thus the stability must be unaffected if the number of transmission lines in operation is changed, if loads are connected or disconnected, or if series compensating devices are introduced into the circuit.

(*d*) Stability must be maintained during any prescribed sequence of operation.

(e) The methods of measuring the quantities which actuate the automatic control must be simple and reliable.

(f) The automatic control system as a whole must have a high degree of reliability in operation.

A satisfactory system must also have the least possible time delay due to inertia in the control devices and in all other components of the excitation system. It is desirable that the exciter current should respond as rapidly as possible to changes of the control signal. The less the time delay, the better the performance of the regulator and the less the variation of voltage.

Recent work has shown that the stability of regulators i has improved and their time delay reduced, resulting in better operation of long lines, when the regulators respond not only to the variations of the controlling signals, (voltage, current, angle) but also to the velocity and acceleration, i.e. to the derivatives of these variations.

Mechanical regulating devices, which have moving parts, are not only subject to time delay, but are also limited in their operation by the so-called *dead zone*; such regulators do not respond to a change of the controlled quantity until the change reaches a certain value. Although the inertia of the moving parts of the regulator also causes a time delay, the effects on the performance of the regulator, of the inertia and of the dead zone, are different in character. Hence, when analysing the operation of electrical systems with automatic control, it is necessary to distinguish between those which have a dead zone and those which do not. The diagram and graphs of Fig. 1.5 illustrate the operation of a system with a dead zone.

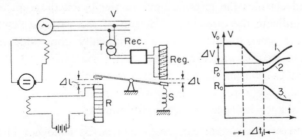

FIG. 1.5. Automatic carbon pile regulator with a dead zone. V — voltage of controlled alternator; T — potential transformer; Rec. — rectifier; Reg. — regulator solenoid; S — spring; (1), voltage variation $V = f(t)$; ΔV — voltage deviation to which the regulator fails to respond due to the air-gap Δl and the inertia of moving parts; (2), change of pressure $P = \psi(t)$; (3), change of resistance of the carbon pile $R = \varphi_1(t)$; Δt_1, time delay in control of pressure and resistance.

Apart from the above requirements an ACS must ensure that the excitation of the alternator is stable under all abnormal conditions, such as no load, overloads up to 20 or 25 per cent, or any condition with forced excitation when the terminal voltage drops appreciably. In order to take care of a failure of any of its components the regulator must incorporate means for transferring the generator automatically to an alternative source of excitation, so as to ensure that the normal power output can be maintained.

An excitation system may comprise automatic devices of different types, provided that they satisfy the above requirements. For example, there may be a device for improving the characteristics of the generator so as to increase its steady-state stability in normal operation. Such a device must have no dead zone, minimum electromagnetic inertia and minimum time delay. Its reliability must be at least as good as that of the generator itself.

A separate device may be used to provide rapidly forced excitation and demagnetization for improving the stability under fault conditions. Immediately after the fault a very rapid rise of exciter voltage and generator field current is required. In order to prevent hunting and loss of stability during the period after the fault, however, the forced excitation must be removed at the correct instant, so that the exciter current is reduced in magnitude or even reversed in direction.

In order to illustrate the action of automatic regulators, which have been discussed above in general terms, consider the very simple AER shown in Fig. 1.6. This brings out the general physical and mathematical concepts and clarifies the terminology. In the block diagram of Fig. 1.6, the arrows indicate the direction of action of the various elements of the system. If the generator were not automatically controlled its terminal voltage would change with changes of load. The operation of the system is considered in relation to the generator terminals, so that the object of the automatic control is to maintain as nearly as possible a constant generator voltage, independent of load changes.

The action of the system can be visualized as follows. The converter element rectifies the output voltage of the instrument transformer connected to the bus-bars. The rectified voltage v is then compared in the measuring element with a reference voltage v_0. The error voltage is applied to the control element, which in turn controls the amplifying element, i.e. the exciters or the rectifiers in an electronic regulator. If the load increases and the voltage falls the exciter field current, and hence the generator excitation, is increased. If, on the other hand, the load decreases and the voltage rises, the exciter acts so as to reduce the voltage.

The generator terminal voltage V_g is the *controlled quantity*, the voltage v_0 is the *reference quantity*, and the difference between them is the

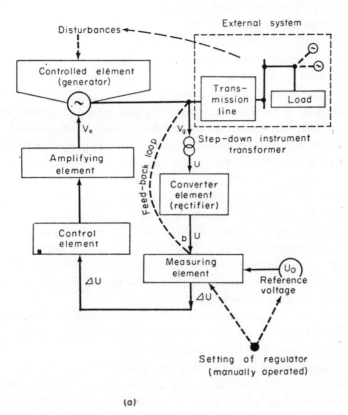

(a)

Fig. 1.6. Block diagram of an automatic excitation regulator.

error, or *deviation*. The generator is the *controlled element*. If the measuring element is sensitive to any change of the controlled quantity, however small, the regulator is said to have no dead zone. If the output of the control element is proportional to the error in the controlled quantity (the generator voltage), the regulator is said to be *linear*. If the measuring element has some moving parts which do not respond to changes of input below a certain value, the regulator is said to have a dead zone. The value of voltage which just fails to operate the measuring element is called the *minimum operating voltage*. It must be emphasized again that any regulator with mechanical parts necessarily has a dead zone.

The excitation system shown in Fig. 1.6 has a closed loop for the control signals and is called a *closed-loop control system*. In this kind of system the measuring element actuates the control element which, by means of the amplifying element, adjusts the magnitude of the controlled quantity. However, the controlled element affects the measuring element, since a change in the generator voltage V_g causes a change in the error voltage Δv which actuates the control element. This interaction between the controlled element and the controlling element is called *negative feedback*. The feed-back acts so as to reduce the difference between the input and the output of the control system.

The measuring element may receive other *external signals* in addition to the *internal signals* due to the closed loop. The external signals may be either *disturbances* or *instructions*. Disturbances arise either in the generator or in the external system, due to changes of load, large or small, switching operations, short circuits, and other changes in the network. The regulator must be able to cope with such conditions when instructions are given to the measuring element by the personnel operating the system. Instructions may be given to change the *setting of the regulator* to maintain a given voltage, or to change the constants of the regulating system to adapt it to changing conditions of operation. Obviously such manual control is undesirable, since, ideally, the ACS should be able to deal with any possible external disturbance.

To produce a signal depending on the error voltage Δv it is now essential to provide a reference voltage; this is usually obtained from a bridge containing non-linear elements.[2,3]

All the interactions in the system represented in Fig. 1.6 are effective in only one direction. Each successive element affects only the following one and the reaction in the other direction is negligible. Such elements constitute an amplifying system. The connexion from the controlled element to the measuring element is called a *negative feed-back connexion*.

Without going into details, it may be mentioned that there may be other types of feed-back. For example, other inter-connexions may be made, in order to improve stability, so that a later element may affect a preceding one. A distinction may be made between a *rigid feed-back*, which is effective under all conditions, and a *loose feed-back*, which acts only during transient changes. Both kinds of feed-back may be either *positive* when, at a given amplification, the action, of the system is speeded up, or *negative* when it is slowed down. The stabilizing types of feed-back are considered here only in so far as they have an effect on the inertia coefficients of the excitation system, increasing or decreasing the rapidity of its response. It may be mentioned that positive feed-back is sometimes used to increase the amplification, in which case the action of the system is retarded.

1.2. Characteristics of Generators [4]

The quantities used to represent the generator differ according to the condition of operation. The effect of the active power (the load) on a generator connected to a simplified system is considered first (Fig. 1.7).

If the excitation of the generator is not automatically controlled, the exciting current and the voltage E_d behind the synchronous reactance

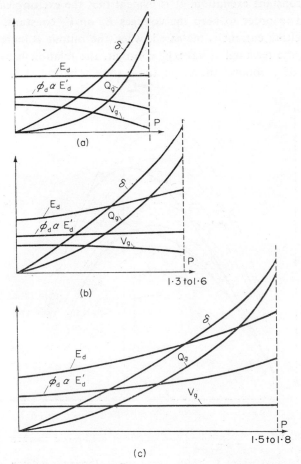

FIG. 1.7. Typical performance curves of a 220 kV transmission system over a line 100–300 km long. (*a*) constant exciting current; (*b*) constant $\Phi_d \infty E'_d$; (*c*) constant terminal voltage V_g.

remain constant during slow changes of load. The other quantities (terminal voltage V_g, voltage E'_d behind the transient reactance, load angle δ, and reactive power Q_g), vary as shown in Fig. 1.7(a).

With a constant field current the transient voltages and the corresponding direct-axis field flux linkages $\Phi_d \propto E'_d$ decrease with increasing load. If the exciting current is controlled so that the transient voltage E'_d remains constant (Fig. 1.7(b)), the maximum power is about 30–60 per cent greater than that of an unregulated generator. If the excitation is controlled so that the terminal voltage V_g is held constant (Fig. 1.7(c)) the maximum power is about 50–80 per cent greater than that of a machine with constant excitation. It is evident that the exciting current must be increased in order to keep the voltages E'_d or V_g constant.

If the exciting current is increased, when the output P increases, so as to maintain the terminal voltage V_g constant, the relation between P and the load angle δ follows the curve (a–e) shown in Fig. 1.8. The curve

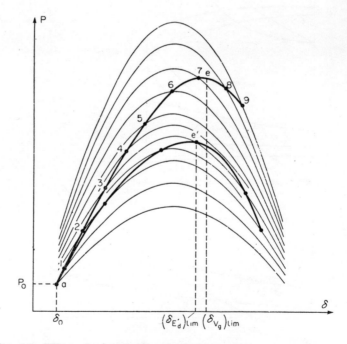

FIG. 1.8. Effect of control of excitation on load-angle characteristics. $P = \dfrac{EV}{x} \sin \delta$, where $E = \varphi(\delta)$; curve (a–e)—forcing regulator maintaining V_g = const; curve (a–e')—normal regulator maintaining E'_d = const.

is no longer sinusoidal, but is the locus of points 1, 2, 3, 4 etc., located on different sinusoidal curves representing the function $P = f(\delta)$ for different values of exciting current. If the increase of excitation is only sufficient to maintain the voltage E'_d constant, the lower curve $(a-e')$ is obtained.

Hence three main types of operation of a power system can be distinguished.

1. *Steady-state characteristic.* The changes of power do not affect the exciting current and the voltage E_d remains constant. This condition applies to an unregulated generator not subjected to rapid changes of load.

2. *Normal transient characteristic.* The voltage E'_d (i.e. the direct-axis flux linkage) is maintained constant. This condition occurs in a regulated

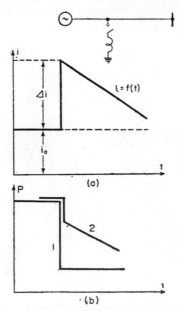

FIG. 1.9. The effect of induced currents in the field winding on the power output. (*a*) change of exciting current after a sudden alteration of load; i_o—forced excitation current; Δi—induced current component; (*b*) power characteristic $P = \varphi(t)$; (1) assuming constant excitation; (2) allowing for the effect of Δi.

machine, and applies at the initial stage of a transient change caused by a sudden change of load. The effective value of the field current is altered by a current induced in the field winding so that the field flux linkages remain constant (Fig. 1.9(*a*)). This type of characteristic is not necessarily a transient one, because it can also apply to a steady-state condition of slowly changing output if an automatic regulator is used (Fig. 1.8, curve (*a–e'*)).

3. *Characteristic with constant terminal voltage.* This condition can only be attained if the excitation is forced so strongly that it provides complete compensation of the armature reactance.

The maximum power under condition (1) is called the *ideal power limit*, while that under conditions (2) and (3) is called the *controlled power limit*. The controlled power limit, obtained by maintaining V_g constant or by retarding its change, ($E_d' = $ const), is achieved by controlling the generator field current. With perfect voltage regulation, i.e. with the terminal voltage constant for all values of load, it is possible to reach the *ideal controlled power limit*.

The three operational characteristics shown in Fig. 1.10 start from the point *a*. If the load changes are slow, each point on any of the character-

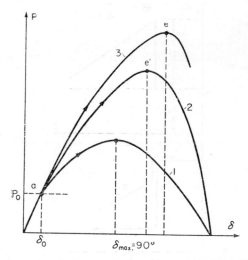

FIG. 1.10. Operational characteristics. (1) steady-state characteristic; exciting current constant. ($E_d = $ const); (2) normal transient characteristic ($E_d' = $ const); (3) characteristic with $V_g = $ const.

istics corresponds to a definite change in the field current. According to the effectiveness of the regulator, different values of voltage and reactance must be used in the equivalent circuit of the generator (E_d and x_d, E_d' and x_d', or V_g with zero internal reactance). Alternatively, there may be some arbitrary condition of regulation of the field current $i_f = f(P)$, for which the generator can be represented by a voltage E_x acting behind a reactance Δx. The relation between these quantities can be determined with the aid of the diagram of Fig. 1.11.

With an increase of the angle δ and the corresponding increase of the power delivered to the line, the terminal voltage falls from its original

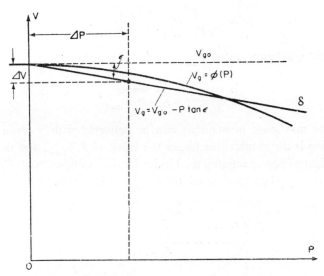

FIG. 1.11. Voltage regulation with load. $V_g = \varphi(P)$, true relation; $V_g = V_{g0} - P \tan \varepsilon$, approximate linear relation.

value V_{g0} at $P = 0$ according to the curve $V_g = \varphi(P)$. If the curve is replaced by the straight line in Fig. 1.11, then

$$V_g = V_{g0}(1 - b_p P),$$

where b_p may be called the *power regulation coefficient* of the line. The power delivered to the line is

$$P = \frac{V_g \cdot V}{x_s} \cdot \sin \delta_s$$

$$= \frac{V_{g0}(1 - b_p P) V}{x_s} \cdot \sin \delta_s$$

$$= \frac{V_{g0} \cdot V}{x_s} \sin \delta_s - \frac{V_{g0} \cdot V}{x_s} b_p \cdot P \cdot \sin \delta_s, \qquad (1.1)$$

where x_s the system reactance and δ_s is the angle between the voltages V and V_g.

In this expression $V_{g0} \cdot V \cdot x_s^{-1}$ is the maximum power $P_{s \cdot \max}$ which would be obtained if V_g were held constant, i.e. under ideal conditions of voltage control.

For a given method of regulation, the relation between the power P and the load angle δ_s is

$$P = \frac{P_{s \cdot \max} \cdot \sin \delta_s}{1 + P_{s \cdot \max} \cdot b_p \cdot \sin \delta_s} \cdot \tag{1.2}$$

P has its maximum value $P_{\max}$ when $\delta_s = 90°$,

$$P_{\max} = \frac{P_{s \cdot \max}}{1 + b_p \cdot P_{s \cdot \max}} \cdot$$

Thus the maximum power that can be delivered with a given method of regulation is the greater, the larger the value of $P_{s \cdot \max}$, and the smaller the coefficient of power regulation. Under ideal conditions, with $V_g = \text{const}$ and $b_p = 0$, $P_{\max}$ becomes equal to $P_{s \cdot \max}$ (Fig. 1.12).

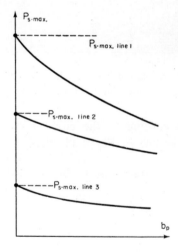

FIG. 1.12. The effect of the coefficient b_p on the maximum power for transmission lines of different limiting power $P_{s \cdot \max}$.

It has been mentioned that the maximum power can be determined by replacing the generator by a certain voltage E_x behind a certain reactance Δx. These two quantities can be determined for given conditions of excitation by writing,

$$P_{\max} = \frac{P_{s \cdot \max}}{1 + b_p \cdot P_{s \cdot \max}} = \frac{E_x \cdot V}{x_s + \Delta x}$$

and

$$E_x = \sqrt{\left(\left[V + \frac{Q_2(x_s+\Delta x)}{V}\right]^2 + \left[\frac{P_{s \cdot max}(x_s+\Delta x)}{V}\right]^2\right)}.$$

Putting $Q_2 = P_{s \cdot max} \cdot \tan \varphi_2$, and assigning values to $\cos \varphi_2$ and b_p, it is possible to determine Δx and V_x for any given value of x_s. Figure 1.13

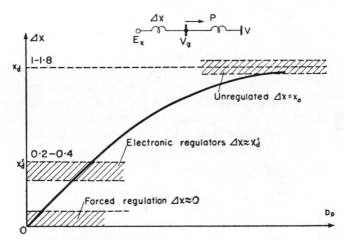

FIG. 1.13. Relation between the coefficient b_p and the equivalent reactance Δx of the generator.

gives the curve relating Δx and b_p. For regulators using electronic devices or compounded machines, which have no dead zone but allow some degree of voltage regulation, the coefficient has a value such that the generator should be replaced by a reactance Δx of the order of 0·2 to 0·4, together with the corresponding voltage E_x behind it. Since the transient reactance is also of the same order, it follows that $E_x \approx E' \approx E_d'$. Thus the maximum power that can be attained by using normal electronic or compounded excitation regulators can be estimated by assuming a constant voltage E_d' behind transient reactance. The special modern electronic excitation regulators, with extra-rapid forcing, which respond not only to the controlled quantity but also to its derivatives, are able to maintain an almost ideally constant voltage ($b_p = 0$), and hence ensure that the system can deliver a maximum power close to the limiting power of the transmission line.

The three types of operation described and the corresponding values of maximum power are based on the assumption that the generator feeds into an infinite bus of constant voltage V. The assumption only holds if the total power rating of the system is much greater (8 to 10 times) than the output to the single station. If the output of the station is comparable with the power rating of the system, the voltage V does not remain constant but falls with increase of load and the maximum power is less.

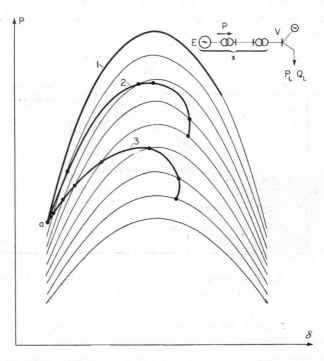

FIG. 1.14. Effect of voltage regulation of load on the power characteris-
tics $P = f(\delta)$. (1) for constant supply voltage ($V = $ const), $P = \dfrac{EV}{x} \cdot \sin \delta$;
(2) for falling supply voltage V and a load with large regulating effect; (3) for falling supply voltage V and a load with smaller regulating effect.

The curves shown in Fig. 1.14 indicate the effect on the shape of the function $P = f(\delta)$ of the reduced value of V. The curve depends particularly on the regulating properties of the load, expressed by its static characteristics $P_L = f(V)$ and $Q_L = f(V)$. The regulation coefficients are defined separately for each of the components of power, namely,

$$a_P = \frac{\Delta P}{\Delta V} \quad \text{and} \quad a_Q = \frac{\Delta Q}{\Delta V} \quad \text{(Fig. 1.15)}$$

which in the limit become

$$a_P = \frac{\mathrm{d}P}{\mathrm{d}V} \quad \text{and} \quad a_Q = \frac{\mathrm{d}Q}{\mathrm{d}V}.$$

The coefficient a_Q has a greater effect on the fall of voltage with increase of transmitted power than the coefficient a_P. This is true not only because

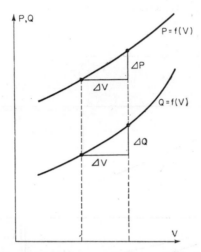

Fig. 1.15. Power-regulation coefficients.

a_Q is usually greater than a_P, but also because, in predominately reactive circuits, the changes of the reactive component of power have a greater effect on the voltage than the changes of the active component, as is apparent from the vector diagrams of Fig. 1.16. The voltage V_P across the load terminals is given by the expression

$$V_L = \sqrt{\left(\left\{ E - \left[\frac{(Q_0 - \Delta Q + 3I_0^2 x)\, x}{E} \right] \right\}^2 + \left\{ \frac{(P_0 - \Delta P)\, x}{E} \right\}^2 \right)},$$

where $\Delta Q = a_Q \Delta V$ and $\Delta P = a_P \Delta V$ are the changes of the power components of the load due to a voltage change ΔV.

Thus, with increasing power P, the greater the regulation coefficients a_Q and a_P, the smaller the regulating effect on the voltage of decrements ΔQ and ΔP.

---

* *Translators' note*: All expressions in the book follow the Russian original. In the expression given above and in several other instances the numerical factor 3 is introduced. Such expressions are inconsistent with the "per-unit" system.

1.3. Characteristics of Prime Movers

The prime movers of a modern electrical power system may be steam or hydraulic turbines, reciprocating steam or internal combustion engines, or wind turbines. In the present book only the first two types are considered, since they are normally used for driving generators in large power systems.

An engineer who designs or operates a power system, often needs to know the general characteristics of a turbogenerator under different

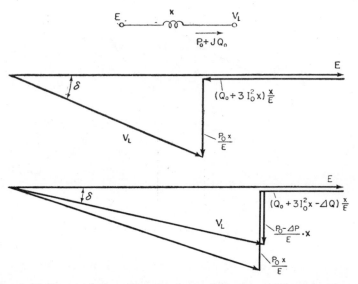

FIG. 1.16. The regulating effect of active and reactive power components.

conditions, and for many purposes the two types of prime movers can be considered to have similar properties. Their operation can be described by the same equations, which relate the changes of speed to changes of torque and power. For such calculations[5] the internal properties of the machines are disregarded, and the turbogenerator is treated as a unit with certain mechanical and electrical characteristics. The different construction of the two types is then reflected in different values of the various constants in equations, which have the same form for both types of turbine.

The first point of interest is the relation between the torque and the speed of the machine, and the dependence of the torque on the quantity of steam or water entering the turbine. In the treatment that follows no distinction is made between steam and water, both of which are considered as the "fluid" supplying the energy.

The diagram, shown in Fig. 1.17, of the turbine and its speed regulator can be used to analyse the interaction between the different parts of the system. Thus the change of fluid flow, caused by a displacement of the piston A of the servo motor, alters the speed of the turbine. The automatic

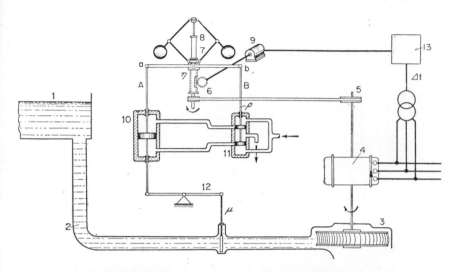

Fig. 1.17. Basic arrangement of a speed-control regulator for a hydraulic or a steam turbine (1) water reservoir producing pressure head (or a steam boiler); (2) pipe line for water (or steam); (3) turbine; (4) generator; (5) drive linking turbine and regulator shafts; (6) regulator shaft; (7) regulator sleeve; (8) regulator sleeve spring; (9) regulator sleeve-motor (speed setting); (10) servo-motor; (11) pilot valve; (12) main inlet valve; (13) automatic frequency and power regulator. A—servo-motor piston, B—pilot-valve piston, μ—displacement of inlet valve, ϱ—displacement of pilot-valve piston, η—displacement of regulator sleeve.

regulator, responding to this change of speed, alters the setting of the main valve. This action, which opposes the action causing the displacement of the piston A, constitutes the main negative feed-back in the regulator. Suppose, for example, that the piston is closing the inlet valve, thus reducing the fluid flow, then the decrease of speed operates the regulator, which tends to slow down the movement of the piston.

In addition to the main negative feed-back, there is a subsidiary negative feed-back through the lever a–b, which connects the piston A of the servo motor to the piston B of the pilot valve. The stability of the regulator is improved by the subsidiary feed-back, which makes it less sensitive to accidental shocks or oscillations that might otherwise cause it to hunt.

The analysis of the system shown in Fig. 1.17 can usefully begin by assuming that the regulator is inoperative and that the torque T_t developed by the turbine is proportional to the displacement μ of the inlet valve 12, which represents the gate of a water turbine or the steam inlet valve of a steam turbine. The assumption can be expressed mathematically by

$$T_t = k_\mu \cdot \mu$$

or graphically by the straight line shown in Fig. 1.18.

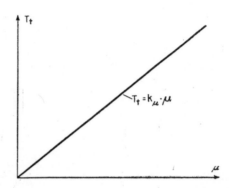

FIG. 1.18. Turbine torque as a function of the displacement of the inlet valve; $T_t = f(\mu)$.

The torque depends not only on the valve opening but also on the speed Ω of the turbine. The relation $T_t = f(\Omega)$ can be expressed for any given value of μ by the equation

$$T_t = (T_t)_0 (1 - k_\Omega \Omega)$$

and shown graphically by the straight line in Fig. 1.19, which cuts the axis at $\Omega = \Omega_{\text{cr}}$. The torque can be expressed as a function of the two variables $T_t = \varphi(\mu, \Omega)$, which for small changes becomes

$$\Delta T_t = \frac{\partial T_t}{\partial \mu} \Delta \mu + \frac{\partial T_t}{\partial \Omega} \Delta \Omega \,.$$

These are *steady-state* characteristics and hold only for slow changes of speed and slow changes of the valve setting. The question arises whether they still apply when the change of the speed or the valve displacement is rapid, i.e. under transient conditions. The difference between the steady-state and transient characteristics of a turbine has not yet been sufficiently investigated. It is generally assumed that for an unregulated

turbine with a constant valve setting, the rate at which the speed changes
(the acceleration) does not affect the relation between the torque and the
speed, i.e. that the steady state and transient characteristics $T_t = f(\Omega)$
are indistinguishable. On the other hand, the rate at which the valve
setting changes can significantly affect the relation $T_t = f(\mu)$; for example,
a rapid closing of the inlet valve of a water turbine can cause water hammer,
while in a steam turbine there may be a further expansion of the steam
trapped by the closed valve. There is therefore an increase of fluid pressure
(water or steam) in front of the closing valve. An opposite effect occurs
if the valve is opened rapidly.

Thus the control of the fluid flow in the turbine depends not only on
the valve opening, which alters the effective cross-section of the pipeline,

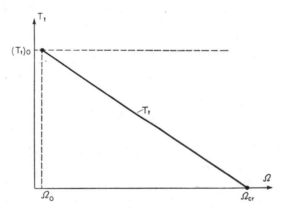

FIG. 1.19. Turbine torque as a function of the speed; $T_t = f(\Omega)$.

but on the pipeline and the turbine itself. Because of this, the changes
of torque and power developed by the turbine do not follow the rapid
changes of the valve setting, as they would if such pressure changes did
not occur.

As shown in Fig. 1.20, rapid closing of the inlet valve brings about
an increase of power developed by the turbine rather than a decrease,
and some time elapses before the turbine power begins to follow the
movement of the valve.

In addition, the change of electrical power supplied by the generator
lags somewhat behind the change of power developed by the turbine
(Fig. 1.20). This occurs during rapid changes of torque, because the increase
of turbine power must not only supply an increase of electrical power, but
must also provide additional kinetic energy to accelerate the rotor.

The important difference between the steady-state and transient characteristic $T_t = f(\mu)$ arises frequently in problems relating to turbine regulation.

In the above discussion of the turbine characteristics it has been assumed that the speed regulator is inoperative. In practice, any departure of the speed from synchronism actuates the regulator. A movement of the sleeve 7 (Fig. 1.17) causes a displacement of the pilot-valve piston B,

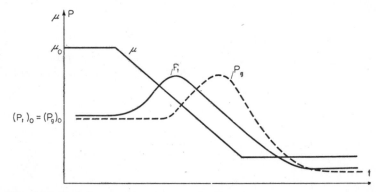

FIG. 1.20. Transient turbine characteristics. μ—inlet valve displacement; P_t—turbine power; P_g—generator power.

thus operating the servo motor 10, which moves the inlet valve 12. The change of the valve setting alters the fluid flow and hence the power developed by the turbine.

The changes of the valve setting and of the power take place relatively slowly. The presence of back-lash and friction can mean that the sleeve does not alter its position (dead zone) if the speed change is relatively small. The sleeve begins to move only when the change of speed exceeds a certain minimum value. Also the effect of the pilot valve on the servo motor and the action of the servo motor itself are subject to delay, because they must overcome appreciable inertia and friction. In general, a normal speed regulator has a delay of about 0·2–0·3 sec before it can begin to affect the power output of its turbine.

In order to obtain a clearer picture of the regulator action, a comparison is made between the operation of unregulated and regulated turbines in Figs. 1.21 and 1.22. In the original steady state, the angular velocity is taken to be Ω_0 and the torque T_0. There is a balance between the mechanical torque of the turbine and the electromagnetic torque of the generator. If for some reason the load on the generator decreases, the mechanical torque is greater than the electrical torque and the set accelerates. With an unregulated turbine this leads to a decrease of mechanical torque, as shown in Fig. 1.21(a). At some point b the mechanical and electrical torques are again equal at a new steady speed Ω_1. Figure 1.21(b) shows the variation of the same quantities with time.

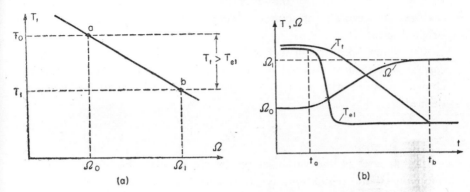

FIG. 1.21. Torque and speed of unregulated turbine. (a) torque speed characteristic $T_t = f(\Omega)$; (b) variation of electrical torque $T_{el} = f(t)$ and the corresponding variation of speed $\Omega = f(t)$.

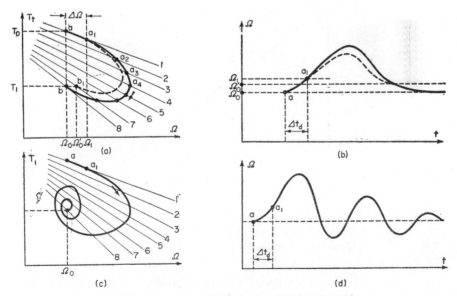

FIG. 1.22. Torque and speed of a regulated turbine.

When a speed regulator is used, the machine follows curve 1 (Fig. 1.22(a)) during the initial stage of the process, which lasts for a time Δt_d, corresponding to the dead zone of the regulator and the delay in the servo-motor. During this time interval the speed changes by $\Delta\Omega$ from Ω_0 to Ω_1. In the next stage the regulator comes into operation, and the operating point of the machine moves from a_1 on curve 1 to a_2, a_3, a_4, etc. on curves 2, 3, 4, etc. At the end of the second stage the regulator establishes either the original speed Ω_0, or some new speed Ω_0' which is usually close to the original speed Ω_0.

If the final speed is, in fact, equal to the original speed, the regulator can be described as *astatic*; otherwise it is *non-astatic*. The greater the change of speed with load, the larger is the *regulation* of the machine, defined as

$$a = \frac{\Omega_0 - \Omega_0'}{\Omega_0}.$$

The manner of the variation of the speed with time, for both astatic and non-astatic regulation, is shown in Fig. 1.22(*b*). If the machine approaches its new speed Ω_0' smoothly and without overshoot, the operation is described as *non-oscillatory*. An *oscillatory* approach, as shown in Figs. 1.22(*c*) and 1.22(*d*), is also possible.

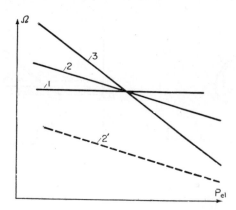

FIG. 1.23. Speed characteristics of a regulated turbine. (1) with an astatic regulator; (2, 3) with non-astatic regulator; (2′) displaced characteristic due to the action of the speed-setting device.

If the relation between speed and load under steady-state conditions is as shown in Fig. 1.23, the slope of the curve is a measure of the regulation *a*.

Thus far it has been assumed that the displacement of the regulator sleeve 7 (Fig. 1.17) is caused only by the change of the turbine speed.

However, the sleeve can also be displaced by the auxiliary motor 9, allowing the speed setting of the regulator to be adjusted. This speed-setting device can be operated either manually or automatically by the frequency control equipment. It usually comes into operation during the third stage of the speed-control process if the frequency of the system is affected by the change of load. The automatic frequency regulator 13, by displacing the sleeve, brings the speed regulator into action and, by adjusting the inlet valve, re-establishes the correct frequency. The displacement of the sleeve by the auxiliary motor corresponds to a displacement of a regulation characteristic parallel to itself, as shown by the dotted curve in Fig. 1.23.

1.4. Characteristics of Loads

An electrical power system supplies a large number of consumers, whose demands make up a complicated system of loads. The load comprises various types of motor (mainly induction motors) amounting to 50–70 per cent of the total, lighting and domestic loads amounting to 20–25 per cent, and transmission losses amounting to 10–12 per cent. Thus the load of the system can be divided into two main parts, the *asynchronous load* and the *lighting load*.

The two kinds of load have both steady-state and transient characteristics. The steady-state characteristics — P, $Q = f(V, f)$ — apply for slow variations of voltage and frequency, while the transient characteristics

$$P, Q = f\left(V, f, \frac{\mathrm{d}V}{\mathrm{d}t}, \frac{\mathrm{d}f}{\mathrm{d}t}\right)$$

apply for rapid changes.

Lighting load

The active power consumed by the lighting load is independent of frequency and varies with voltage approximately as $V^{1\cdot6}$. Such load consumes no reactive power. For the analysis of transient conditions the transient characteristics of this type of load can be taken to be identical with its steady-state characteristics. The lighting load can therefore be represented by a single characteristic $P = f(V)$, shown in Fig. 1.24, which also shows the corresponding change of the effective resistance. Figure 1.25 shows the variation of P when the voltage varies rapidly.

Asynchronous load

The steady-state and transient characteristics of asynchronous loads
are different. The difference arises because there are induced currents

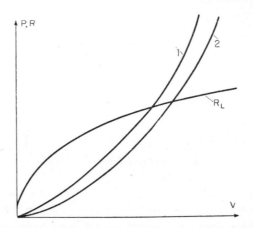

Fig. 1.24. Power supplied to a lighting load as a function of voltage.
(1) for constant load resistance R_L; (2) for variable load resistance
$R_L = f(V)$.

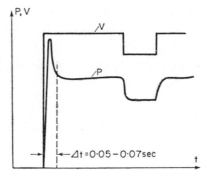

Fig. 1.25. Power fluctuations in a lighting load caused by sudden
changes of voltage.

when the slip changes rapidly. Figure 1.26(*a*) shows a three-dimensional
diagram of the torque characteristics, and Fig. 1.26(*b*) shows a family
of curves, which are more convenient for practical design.

If the time rate of change of slip is not too large, the transient characteristics of an induction motor for changing conditions of operation, e.g.
for a variable supply voltage, can be derived from a family of its steady-
state characteristics. The method of doing this is indicated below.

When considering the steady-state characteristics of an induction motor, the problem is simplified if the stator losses are not included, but are either lumped with the line losses or combined with those of the rotor

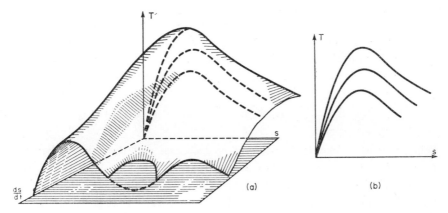

FIG. 1.26. Induction-motor torque as a function of slip s and acceleration d s/dt.

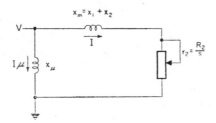

FIG. 1.27. Simplified equivalent circuit for an induction motor.

(with $r_2 = R_2/s$). If the magnetizing losses are also neglected, the induction motor may be represented by the simplified equivalent circuit shown in Fig. 1.27.

The active power taken by the motor and the torque developed are determined under these conditions by the mechanical torque demanded by the driven mechanism, i.e. by its characteristic $T_{mech} = f(s)$. The changes of P and T depend on the characteristics of the supply and of the driven mechanisms.

To simplify matters it is assumed that the mechanical torque T_{mech} is independent of the slip. All the equations are henceforth expressed in per-unit quantities. Hence for steady conditions, neglecting losses, $P_{mech} = T_{mech}$, and

$$P_{\text{el}} = P_{\text{mech}} = P = 3I^2 \frac{R_2}{s} = \text{const.}$$

$$\text{Hence,} \quad s = 3\frac{I^2 R_2}{P}, \quad \text{or} \quad s \propto I^2.$$

The equivalent circuit of Fig. 1.27 shows that the reactive power Q taken by the motor consists of two components, Q_μ the magnetizing power associated with the magnetizing current I_μ, and Q_s associated with the stator and rotor leakage. Hence, with the above assumptions,

$$Q_\mu = \frac{V^2}{x_\mu}, \quad Q_s = 3I^2 x_m, \quad \text{and} \quad Q = Q_\mu + Q_s.$$

When saturation occurs the value of x_μ decreases and the relation between Q_μ and V departs appreciably from a square law.

The relation between the supply voltage and the slip is readily obtained from the equivalent circuit of Fig. 1.27.

$$P = 3I^2 \frac{R_2}{s} = \frac{V^2}{\left(\dfrac{R_2}{s}\right)^2 + x_m^2} \cdot \frac{R_2}{s} = \frac{V^2 \cdot R_2 \cdot s}{R_2^2 + (s\, x_m)^2}. \tag{1.3}$$

Figure 1.28 gives a family of curves showing this relation for various values of the voltage V. The relation between s and V, for a given value of P, is also shown in Fig. 1.28. Since $Q = 3I^2 x_m$, and $I^2 \propto s$ for a constant mechanical torque, the relation $Q_s = f(V)$ has the same shape as the relation $s = f(V)$, as shown in Fig. 1.29.

These curves show that, for any given value of the mechanical load P_{mech}, the motor has a critical slip s_{cr} and critical voltage V_{cr}. The maximum power P_{max} which the motor can develop is then exactly equal to the mechanical power demanded, and operation at a lower voltage is not possible, because the electrical power would then be less than the mechanical power.

The critical slip and critical power are determined mathematically by differentiating the expression for P in equation (1.3) with respect to s and equating to zero.

$$\frac{dP}{dS} = V^2 R_2 \cdot \frac{R_2^2 - (s\, x_m)^2}{[R_2^2 + (s\, x_m)^2]^2} = 0,$$

whence,

$$s_{\text{cr}} = \frac{R_2}{x_m} \tag{1.4}$$

$$P_{\max} = \frac{V^2}{2x_m}.$$ (1.5)

Figure 1.29 shows the curve of $Q_\mu = f(V)$, the curve of $Q_s = f(V)$, and the curve of total reactive power $Q = Q_\mu + Q_s = f(V)$. The point

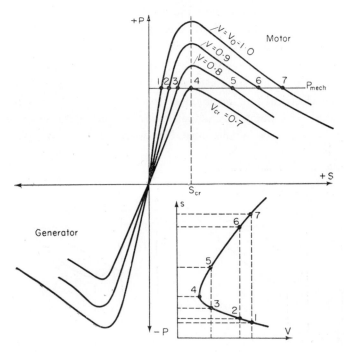

FIG. 1.28. Power-slip characteristics for an induction motor $P = f(s)$ and the corresponding slip-voltage characteristic $s = f(V)$.

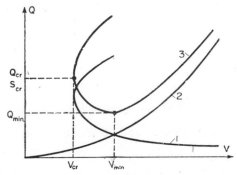

FIG. 1.29. Reactive power component-voltage characteristic for an induction motor. (1) $Q_s = f(V)$; (2) $Q_\mu = f(V)$; (3) $Q_s + Q_\mu = f(V)$.

$Q = Q_{cr}$, $V = V_{cr}$, at which $dQ/dV = -\infty$, or $dV/dQ = 0$, corresponds to operation at the point 4 on Fig. 1.28.

It may be noted that, if the slip is less than the critical value, dP/ds is always positive and the motor operation is stable. Any accidental change of the slip, or of the rotor angle, brings about an imbalance between the electrical accelerating torque and the mechanical braking torque, causing the rotor to return to the original condition of operation. It can be easily seen that this occurs at the points 1, 2, 3, of Fig. 1.28.

On the other hand, at points 5, 6, 7, the value of dP/ds is negative and the operation is unstable, since a small change of slip increases the imbalance between the electrical and mechanical torques and leads to a further increase in slip. The point 4 is of particular interest, because it lies at the boundary between stable and unstable operation.

Steady-state load characteristics

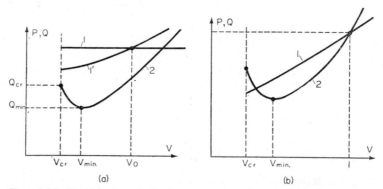

(a)   (b)

FIG. 1.30. Steady-state load characteristics. (*a*) for induction motor load; $1 - P = f(V)$, losses neglected; $1' - P = f(V)$, losses included; $2 - Q = f(V)$; (*b*) for composite load; $1 - P = f(V)$; $2 - Q = f(V)$.

The total load characteristics for both active and reactive power can be obtained by adding together the lighting load, the motor load, and the power losses in the cables and transformers. Typical characteristics for an induction motor are shown in Fig. 1.30(*a*) and for a composite load in Fig. 1.30(*b*). These show that for typical loads at normal voltage, the slope $\dfrac{dP}{dV}$ varies between 0·5 and 0·75, and the slope $\dfrac{dQ}{dV}$ varies between 1·5 and 2·5.

The composite load supplied by a power system can, for calculation purposes, be represented either by an equivalent circuit which includes lighting and induction motor loads or by characteristics derived from an equivalent circuit. The characteristics can then be further simplified, as shown in Fig. 1.31. In Fig. 1.31(*a*), it is assumed that the active power *P* and the reactive power *Q* are either constant or are linearly related to the voltage. In Fig. 1.31(*b*), both *P* and *Q* are assumed to vary as the square

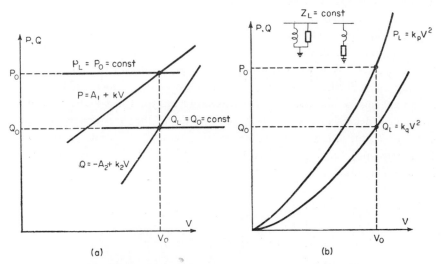

FIG. 1.31. Alternative ways of representing load characteristics.
(*a*) linear approximations; (*b*) square-law approximations.

of the voltage. With the latter assumption the equivalent impedance Z_L of the total load may be represented either by a parallel or a series equivalent circuit. For the parallel circuit

$$R_L = \frac{V^2}{P_L}, \qquad x_L = \frac{V^2}{Q_L}.$$

For the series circuit,

$$Z_L = R_L \pm jx_L = \frac{V^2}{\bar{S}} = \frac{V^2}{S}(\cos \varphi \pm j \sin \varphi)$$

where $\bar{S}$ is the total complex power supplied to the load and S is its modulus.

These simplifications have a certain range of practical application. The simplest assumption, that the power is independent of the voltage, is appropriate for steady-state calculations. Such calculations start by assuming the power delivered at various points in the network to be independent of the voltage. The assumption is justified if the voltage at the customers' terminals is maintained constant, independently of any variation of the voltage of the high-voltage transmission line. The customers' voltage would be held constant by changing transformer taps or by using static or synchronous condensers.

It is obvious that the characteristics $P = $ const and $Q = $ const are not applicable to transient conditions. The use of approximate steady-state characteristics, taking the tangents $(A_1 + k_1 V)$ and $(-A_2 + k_2 V)$ as in Fig. 1.31(a), gives good results for transient conditions only if the voltage variations are small. Otherwise the error is likely to be considerable.

The power taken by a composite load also varies with frequency. As already mentioned, an ordinary lighting load is independent of frequency, although this is not true for gas-discharge lamps, for which the power, consumed decreases by 0·5–0·8 per cent, if the frequency increases by 1 per cent. In general, however, the manner of variation of power with frequency for a composite load is determined almost entirely by its induction motor component.

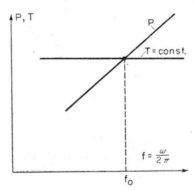

FIG. 1.32. Dependence of real power P taken by an induction motor on the frequency at constant torque T.

If the output torque T_{mech} at the motor shaft is constant, the active power P taken by the motor is proportional to the frequency. $P = \omega T$ (Fig. 1.32).

For an induction motor with normal design constants, a drop in frequency causes a drop in slip, as shown in Fig. 1.33, according to

$$T = \frac{V^2 R_2 s}{\left[R_2^2 + \left(\frac{\omega}{\omega_0} \cdot s x_0 \right)^2 \right] \omega}$$

or, very approximately, $s \propto f$, if T is constant.

The reactive power taken by the motor also varies with frequency. To determine the manner of variation it is necessary to consider separately the frequency characteristics of its two components Q_s and Q_μ.

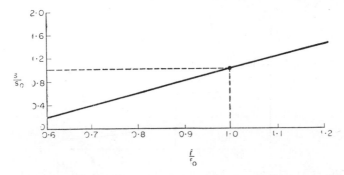

FIG. 1.33. Slip-frequency characteristic for an induction motor.

Taking
$$s = 3 \frac{I^2 R_2}{\omega T} \quad \text{and} \quad Q_s = 3 I^2 \frac{x_0}{\omega_0} \omega,$$

it follows that
$$I^2 \propto \omega s \quad \text{and} \quad Q_s \propto \omega^2 s \propto f_s^2.$$

Thus Q_s decreases when the frequency falls and increases when the frequency rises.

The other component of the reactive power Q_μ increases with decreasing frequency, since
$$Q_\mu = \frac{V^2}{\dfrac{x_{\mu_0}}{\omega_0} \cdot \omega} \propto \frac{1}{f}.$$

For a normal induction motor the variation of the total reactive power $Q = Q_s + Q_\mu$ is determined mainly by the first component when the change of frequency is small, but the second component is important when there is a considerable rise of frequency (Fig. 1.34).

Figure 1.35 gives frequency characteristics for a typical composite load. They show that at nominal voltage ($V = 1$) and at nominal frequency the value of the slope dQ/df is about -0.8 to -1.2, while that of the slope dP/df is about 1.7 to 2.5.

Hitherto it has been assumed that the variations of voltage and frequency are independent of each other. In practice, however, frequency changes are often accompanied by voltage changes. A variation of frequency is usually caused by an imbalance between the electrical output of the generators and the mechanical output of the prime movers. The change of frequency, as shown above, changes the reactive power taken by the load and the

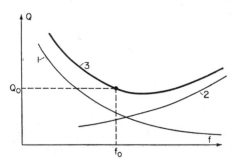

FIG. 1.34. The change of reactive power component Q taken by an induction motor with change of frequency. (1) $Q_\mu = \varphi(f)$; (2) $Q_s = \varphi((f)$; (3) $(Q_s + Q_\mu) = \varphi(f)$.

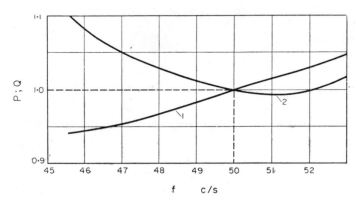

FIG. 1.35. Composite-load frequency characteristics. (1) $P = \varphi(f)$; (2) $Q = \varphi(f)$.

active and reactive power losses in the network, and hence causes a change of voltage. A decrease of frequency generally causes a decrease of voltage. The curves in Fig. 1.36 show how the active and reactive power components change when the frequency and voltage vary simultaneously.

Assuming a given value of the shaft torque T_{mech}, the curves show that, for a frequency below normal, the maximum electrical torque and the critical slip increase, while the operating slip decreases. Thus a decrease of frequency affects the motor operation in a manner similar to an increase of voltage. Consequently, if the frequency is below normal, a larger drop of voltage can be tolerated without danger of losing stability. In other words, the critical voltage is lower if the frequency is below normal.

This effect is illustrated in Fig. 1.36(*b*), which shows the displacement of the characteristic $Q = f(V)$ due to a change of frequency and the corresponding shift of the point at which $dQ/dV = \infty$. Thus the lowering of

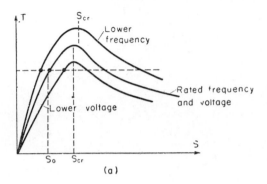

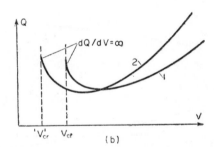

FIG. 1.36. Torque, critical slip, and reactive power as functions of frequency. (*a*) $T = f(s)$; (*b*) $Q = f(V)$: $1 - f = f_0$ $2 - f < f_0$.

the frequency and the consequent decrease of power demand (Fig. 1.35) and of the critical voltage can be regarded as desirable properties, which tend to improve the stability of a heavily loaded system operating below normal voltage. However, this kind of operation is not acceptable, except in quite abnormal conditions which sometimes occurred during the Second World War.

Stability of loads

The earlier discussion shows that the zone of stable operation of an induction motor extends from synchronous speed to a speed corresponding to the critical value of slip s_{cr}. The zone between $s = s_{cr}$ and $s = 1$ is one of unstable operation. Under normal conditions the motor operates on the stable part of its characteristic, between the points a_1 and a_1' on Fig. 1.37(a), with a slip less than the critical value. If, however, the voltage is less than normal, or the shaft torque increases, the motor may

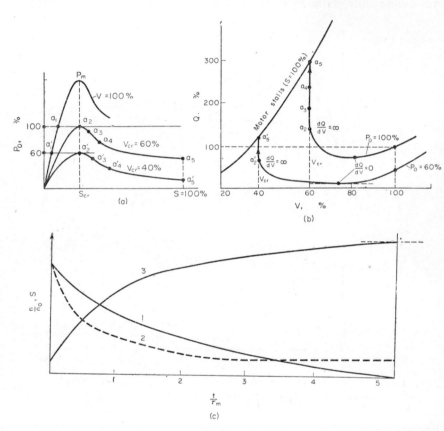

Fig. 1.37. Induction motor characteristics (a) $P = f(s)$ at various values of constant input voltage; (b) $Q = f(V)$, derived from the characteristics $P = f(s)$; (c) stalling process as a function of time (τ_m — mechanical time constant); (1) speed ratio $\dfrac{n}{n_0} = f(t)$; (2) impedance; (3) input current.

operate at a critical point a_2. The slightest fall of voltage can then move the operating point to the falling part of the characteristic (points a_3 and a_4), so that the motor slows down and eventually stalls.

The process of stalling at the critical voltage is illustrated in Figs. 1.37(b) and 1.37(c). Induction motors normally have a very wide margin of stability. The slip during normal operation is much less than the critical value, and the maximum torque is much greater than the full-load torque (1·5 to 1·7 times). Hence the normal fluctuations of voltage are not dangerous from the point of view of stability, and the motor stalls only if the terminal voltage falls by as much as 30 to 40 per cent.

So far only a single motor, or group of motors, supplied at constant voltage, has been considered. If, however, the motor is fed from a generator of comparable power output, so that the terminal voltage of the generator is affected by the operation of the motor, the stalling conditions are changed

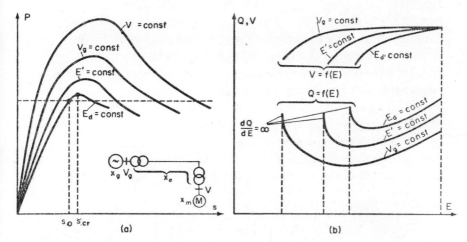

FIG. 1.38. Power characteristics of several induction motors of combined power comparable to the generator output. The characteristics are constructed on the assumption that either E_d, E' or V_g are independent of the motor load; (a) $P = f(s)$; (b) $Q = f(E)$.

considerably (Fig. 1.38) The generator reactance x_g, the line reactance x_e, and the motor reactance x_m, are of comparable magnitude. The maximum torque is

$$T_{max} = \frac{1}{2}\left(\frac{E^2}{x_g + x_e + x_m}\right)$$

and the critical slip is

$$s_{cr} = \frac{R}{x_g + x_e + x_m},$$

where E is the internal voltage of the generator. The curves of Fig. 1.38 show that under such conditions stalling of the motor may be caused by relatively small changes of slip or voltage.

The critical conditions are determined not by the terminal voltage of the motor, but rather by some equivalent voltage E behind an appropriate reactance, the voltage being assumed to be independent of the motor load. For an unregulated generator the voltage is E_d, for one regulated by ordinary means it is $E'_d \simeq E'$, and for one provided with extra-rapid regulation V_g. The characteristics $V = f(E)$ and $Q = f(E)$ corresponding to these cases are shown in Fig. 1.38(b).

It can be seen that a decrease in the voltage E, particularly in the region of negative values of dQ/dE, leads to an increase of the reactive power and of the line voltage drop, and hence reduces the motor voltage still further. Near the stalling point of the motor, the rapid reduction of voltage is particularly marked. The operators in a station or sub-station have no direct evidence that the motors may be operating near to their stalling point, but are faced with a rapid fall in voltage. This condition of instability may be termed a *collapse of voltage*. It can be brought about either by insufficient excitation, or by an increase of the effective reactance of the connected system. The operators, however, tend to assume quite erroneously that the voltage collapses primarily because the reactive power produced by the generator is reduced.

The equivalent circuit of Fig. 1.39(a) can be used to obtain a quantitative assessment of the conditions leading to the collapse of voltage, and to

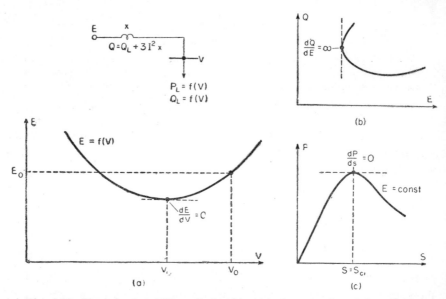

FIG. 1.39. Three load-stability criteria. (a) equivalent circuit and the relation between the equivalent voltage E and the terminal voltage V across the composite load; (b) $Q = f(E)$; (c) $P = f(s)$.

estimate the margin of stability of the motors. In this circuit the system generators are replaced by a single constant voltage source. It is usually very difficult to specify definite constants for the equivalent load, which contains all kinds of consumers' equipment, and it is much simpler and more convenient to use for this purpose the steady-state load characteristics discussed earlier in this section.

Instead of using the stability criterion $dP/ds = 0$, or the equivalent criterion $dQ/dE = \infty$, it appears preferable to introduce another secondary criterion $dE/dV = 0$. Figure 1.39(a) shows that, at the critical value of the motor terminal voltage, the derivative dE/dV becomes equal to zero, resulting in loss of stability. This result follows from the equivalent circuit shown in Fig. 1.39(a), where the voltage V at the terminals of the composite load depends on the motor operation, while the equivalent voltage E is treated as the independent variable.

The relation between the two voltages is readily obtained as follows.

$$V = \sqrt{\left[\left(E - \frac{Q\,x}{E}\right)^2 + \left(\frac{Px}{E}\right)^2\right]} \simeq E - \frac{Qx}{E}$$

where Q is the internal reactive power of the generator.
Hence

$$\frac{dV}{dE} = 1 - \frac{\left(E\dfrac{dQ}{dE} - Q\right)x}{E^2}\,.$$

It follows that, when dQ/dE tends to ∞, dV/dE also tends to ∞, and dE/dV tends to zero. The margin of stability can be assessed from the ratio of the actual terminal voltage to the critical voltage for which $dE/dV = 0$.

It is convenient to determine the margin of stability of a composite load by constructing the curve $E = f(V)$, using the known steady-state load characteristics $P_L = f(V)$ and $Q_L = f(V)$. This method is reasonably simple and gives a good estimate of the margin of stability.

Figure 1.40 illustrates the behaviour of a system when it becomes unstable. It shows the effect of throwing off a part of the load and of forcing the generator excitation.

It is clear that the use of regulators, which maintain a high equivalent voltage, or even a constant generator terminal voltage, brings about a reduction of the critical voltage. In the limit, with constant generator voltage and a very short line, the critical voltage is that determined at the motor terminals.

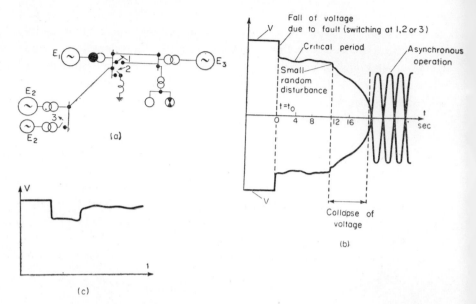

FIG. 1.40. Instability of a system leading to a collapse of voltage. (*a*) circuit diagram of the system; operations which may lead to collapse of voltage: at 1, disconnexion of part of the transmission network; at 2, connexion of an inductive load; at 3, disconnexion of some generating plant; (*b*) behaviour of an unregulated system; (*c*) behaviour of a system with forced excitation.

Electrical centre of a system

There is a danger of loss of stability when a load is located at the electrical centre of a power system. When the generators hunt, or operate asynchronously, the voltages at the various points of the system network change. In any system, for a given condition, there is a point at which the voltage is a minimum. This point is defined as the *electrical centre* of the system.

If the system is fully symmetrical, as in the diagram of Fig. 1.41, with two generators of equal and constant voltage and line elements of the same R/x ratio, the electrical centre of the system corresponds to its geometrical centre. The voltage at this point is equal to zero if the system voltages have a phase displacement of 180°. A consumer at the electrical centre may therefore sometimes be placed in a condition equivalent to a short circuit ($V = 0$), leading to incorrect operation of the protective gear. If the operation of the protective devices is determined by the effective impedance of the line $Z_L = V/I$, (distance relays), undamaged sections of the line may become disconnected.

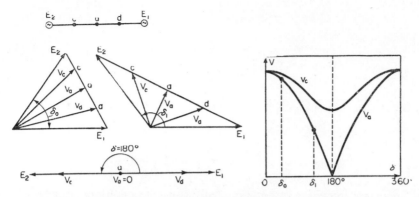

FIG. 1.41. Electrical centre of a system.

An actual power system never possesses such a high degree of symmetry, and the concept of the electrical centre is less well defined. The location of the electrical centre may be anywhere along the line, or it may be inside a generator, a transformer, or a load. Moreover, its position in the system may change when hunting occurs.

CHAPTER 2

LARGE DISTURBANCES ASSOCIATED WITH LARGE VARIATIONS OF SPEED

2.1. General Characteristics and Basic Equations

There are many important practical transient conditions, during which the generator speed departs considerably from synchronous speed, for example:

(a) Asynchronous operation of a synchronous machine, caused by loss of excitation.

(b) Resynchronization, after a period of instability.

(c) Self-synchronization of a generator.

(d) Automatic reclosing of switches, causing self-synchronization, or uncontrolled synchronization.

(e) Starting from rest of synchronous motors, condensers, or generators.

In the study of these conditions it is important, first of all, to determine the nature of the changes in the elements of the system and in the parameters representing them, when appreciable changes of speed occur.

Generator characteristics

When the change of speed is appreciable, the power and the electrical torque developed in a synchronous machine, operating either as a generator or a motor, depend not only on the load angle, but also on the time rate of change of the load angle. Both the power P and the torque T can then, as an approximation, be considered to be made up of a synchronous component and an asynchronous component.

$$P = P_s + P_{as}^{\cdot} \quad \text{and} \quad T = T_s + T_{as}.$$

The synchronous power component P_s depends on the constants applicable to synchronous operation, and on the applied voltage, the excitation, and the load angle δ. The asynchronous component P_{as} depends on the asynchronous constants, and on the applied voltage, the load angle δ, and on its time rate of change, i.e. the slip s. The slip is defined as $s = -\,\mathrm{d}\delta/\mathrm{d}t$, and is therefore positive for speeds below synchronous speed.

The synchronous power component P_s is determined in the same way as during synchronous operation, except that the per-unit torque and power cannot now be assumed equal to each other. They are related by the equation

$$T_s = \frac{P_s}{1-s}.$$

The asynchronous power component $P_{as} = T_{as}$ is determined by assuming that it is independent of the excitation, and that the two components of power and torque can be added together, after their values have been obtained separately. This assumption is not strictly true, and the result obtained is only a first approximation.

It is assumed below that the synchronous machine has electrical and magnetic symmetry, i.e. that its direct-axis and quadrature-axis constants are equal.

$$\tau'_q = \tau'_d \; ; \quad x_q = x_d \; ; \quad x'_q = x'_d \; .$$

If the machine operates with a constant or slowly changing slip, the power can be determined by treating the machine as an induction motor,

$$P_{as} = - \frac{V^2 \cdot R \cdot s}{R^2 + (xs)^2} = T_{as} . \tag{2.1}$$

At positive values of slip, equation (2.1) gives the power taken from the supply (motor action), while at negative values of slip it gives the power delivered to the supply (generator action). R and x are the asynchronous constants in a simplified equivalent circuit which represents the machine when operating asynchronously. The constants of an alternator are not usually given in this form in reference books, and it is therefore convenient to rewrite equation (2.1) in terms of the synchronous machine constants.[6] If the damper windings are ignored, the torque is given by

$$T_{as} = - \frac{V^2(x_d - x'_d)}{x_d \cdot x'_d} \cdot \frac{s\tau'_d}{1 + (s\tau'_d)^2} , \tag{2.2}$$

where

$$\frac{R}{x} \simeq \frac{1}{\tau'_d} , \quad \text{and} \quad \frac{1}{x} \simeq \frac{1}{x'_d} - \frac{1}{x_d} .$$

At small values of slip, a very rough approximation can often be made.

$$T_{as} = P_{as} = sP_d ,$$

where

$$P_d = - \frac{V^2(x_d - x'_d)}{x_d \cdot x'_d} \cdot \tau'_d , \quad \text{or}$$

$$P_d = - \frac{V^2(x_d - x'_d)}{x_d^2} \tau_{d0}(s),$$

where

$$\tau_{d0}(s) = \varphi \left(\frac{d\delta}{dt} \right).$$

When the rotor is not symmetrical, as is normally the case, the active and reactive components of the asynchronous power pulsate, as shown in Fig. 2.1. The instantaneous asynchronous torque, which is nearly equal

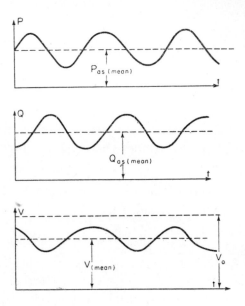

FIG. 2.1. Active and reactive power components of a generator operating asynchronously and the voltage fluctuation caused thereby.

to the asynchronous power, when steady asynchronous operation is established, is given by equation (2.2a), in which the second and third terms are due to the damper winding.

$$P_{as} = T_{as} = \frac{V^2}{2} \left\{ - \frac{x_d - x_d'}{x_d \cdot x_d'} \cdot \frac{s\tau_d'}{1 + (s\tau_d')^2} \cdot \right.$$

$$\cdot \left[1 + \sqrt{\{1 + (s\tau_d')^2\}} \cdot \sin\left(2\delta_0 - \arctan \frac{1}{s\tau_d'} - 2st\right) \right] -$$

$$- \frac{x_d' - x_d''}{x_d' \cdot x_d''} \cdot \frac{s\tau_d''}{1 + (s\tau_d'')^2} \cdot \left[1 - \sqrt{\{1 + (s\tau_d'')^2\}} \cdot \sin\left(2\delta_0 - \arctan \frac{1}{s\tau_d''} - 2st\right) \right] -$$

$$- \frac{x_q - x_q''}{x_q \cdot x_q''} \cdot \frac{s\tau_q''}{1 + (s\tau_q'')^2} \cdot \left[1 - \sqrt{\{1 + (s\tau_q'')^2\}} \sin\left(2\delta_0 - \arctan \frac{1}{s\tau_q''} - 2st\right) \right] \right\},$$

$$(2.2a)$$

where the values of arc tan $1/s\tau$ lie between 0 and 180°.

The corresponding mean value of the asynchronous torque $T_{as(mean)}$, is given by

$$P_{as(mean)} \simeq T_{as(mean)} = -\frac{V^2}{2} \cdot s \cdot$$

$$\cdot \left[\frac{x_d - x_d'}{x_d \cdot x_d'} \cdot \frac{\tau_d'}{1 + (s\tau_d')^2} + \frac{x_d' - x_d''}{x_d' \cdot x_d''} \cdot \frac{\tau_d''}{1 + (s\tau_d'')^2} + \frac{x_q - x_q''}{x_q \cdot x_q''} \cdot \frac{\tau_q''}{1 + (s\tau_q'')^2} \right]. \quad (2.2b)$$

These expressions for the asynchronous torque remain valid also for a generator feeding into an infinite bus through an external reactance x_L (Fig. 2.2a), if x_L is added to the leakage reactance of the alternator when the reactances and time constants are calculated. They can also be used for approximate calculations in which the system is replaced by

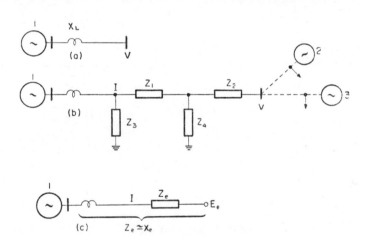

Fig. 2.2. Equivalent circuit for a system when one of its stations (1) runs asynchronously. (*a*) simplified equivalent circuit; station 1 connected to an infinite bus of voltage V; (*b*) station 1 connected to an infinite bus through a complicated network; (*c*) the equivalent circuit in which the voltage V is no longer considered constant and all loads and stations (excepting station 1) are replaced by an equivalent impedance Z_e and an equivalent voltage E_e.

an equivalent generator having a fixed voltage E_e behind a reactance x_e, as shown in Fig. 2.2(*c*).

The reactive power taken by a synchronous generator operating asynchronously is an important quantity. Thus an excessive demand for reactive power can produce an appreciable voltage drop in the system, causing difficulties for the consumers or instability of the power stations supplying the system (voltage collapse or inferior steady-state or transient stability in the receiving network).

In the very simple case, for which the expressions (2.1) and (2.2) were derived, the idealized symmetrical generator operating asynchronously was replaced by an equivalent circuit containing series and shunt branches. The reactive power Q_{as} taken by the shunt reactance x, is then equal to the reactive power suppplied by the network (the magnetizing power is not allowed for, because it is included in the expression for the synchronous power component of the generator):

$$Q_{as} = \frac{xs^2V^2}{R^2+(sx)^2} .$$
(2.3)

From the relations (2.1) and (2.2) it follows that

$$\frac{x_d-x_d'}{x_d \cdot x_d'} \cdot \frac{\tau_d'}{1+(s\tau_d')^2} = \frac{R}{R^2+(sx)^2} ,$$
(2.4)

so that it is possible to express the reactive component of power Q_{as} in terms of the synchronous constants of the generator

$$Q_{as} = \frac{x}{R} \cdot s^2 \cdot \frac{x_d-x_d'}{x_d \cdot x_d'} \cdot \frac{\tau_d'}{1+(s\tau_d')^2} \cdot V^2 =$$

$$= \frac{x_d-x_d'}{x_d \cdot x_d'} \cdot \frac{(s\tau_d')^2}{1+(s\tau_d')^2} \cdot V^2, \text{ or}$$
(2.5)

$$Q_{as} = P_{as} \frac{s}{s_{cr}} .$$

In addition to the asynchronous components of power P_{as} and Q_{as}, the generator operating at a slip s develops synchronous components P_s and Q_s dependent on the excitation and on the angle δ.

Assuming that the slip is constant, and writing for the angle δ,

$$\delta = -\int_0^t sdt = -st ,$$

the active power component P_s developed during asynchronous operation, is given by

$$P_s = \frac{E_d \cdot V}{x_{dt}} \cdot \sin st,$$
(2.6)

where

$$x_{dt} = x_d+x_e .$$

Here E_d is the voltage induced in the generator at synchronous speed due to the excitation voltage. Thus the synchronous power is due to the steady exciting current, while the asynchronous power is due to the induced rotor currents which depend on the slip.

An alternative expression is:

$$P_s = \frac{E_d' \cdot V}{x_{dt}'} \sin st - \frac{1}{2} V^2 \cdot \frac{x_d - x_d'}{x_{dt}' \cdot x_{dt}} \cdot \sin 2st, \qquad (2.7)$$

where

$$x_{dt}' = x_d' + x_e .$$

The reactive component of synchronous power Q_s, when the regulator is absent, is given by the expression,

$$Q_s = \frac{E_d \cdot V}{x_{dt}} \cos st - \frac{V^2}{x_{dt}}, \qquad (2.8)$$

where the second term represents the reactive power Q_μ required for magnetization.

The sum of the expressions in (2.2) and (2.6) gives the active component of the total power developed during asynchronous operation and the sum of the expressions in (2.5) and (2.8) gives the reactive component of power.

For an asymmetrical machine ($x_d \neq x_q$, $x_d' \neq x_q'$ etc.), the active component of synchronous power is given by

$$\left.\begin{aligned}
P_s &= \frac{E_d \cdot V}{x_{dt}} \sin st + \frac{1}{2} V^2 \frac{x_d - x_q}{x_{dt} \cdot x_{qt}} \sin 2st , \\[2mm]
P_s &= \frac{E_d' \cdot V}{x_{dt}} \sin st + \frac{1}{2} V^2 \frac{x_q - x_d'}{x_{dt}' \cdot x_{qt}} \sin 2st
\end{aligned}\right\}. \qquad (2.9)$$

or by

In absence of the regulator, the total reactive power Q (synchronous, asynchronous and magnetizing components) is given by $Q = Q_s + Q_\mu' + Q_{as}$, or

$$\begin{aligned}
Q = {} & \frac{V E_d}{x_{dt}} \cos st - \frac{V^2}{2} \left\{ \frac{1}{x_{dt}} + \frac{1}{x_{qt}} - \left(\frac{1}{x_{qt}} - \frac{1}{x_{dt}} \right) \cos 2st + \right. \\[2mm]
& + \left(\frac{1}{x_{dt}'} - \frac{1}{x_{dt}} \right) \left[\frac{(s\tau_d')^2}{1+(s\tau_d')^2} + \frac{s\tau_d'}{\sqrt{[1+(s\tau_d')^2]}} \cos \left(2st - \arctan \frac{1}{s\tau_d'} \right) \right] + \\[2mm]
& + \left(\frac{1}{x_{dt}''} - \frac{1}{x_{dt}'} \right) \left[\frac{(s\tau_d'')^2}{1+(s\tau_d'')^2} + \frac{s\tau_d''}{\sqrt{[1+(s\tau_d'')^2]}} \cos \left(2st - \arctan \frac{1}{s\tau_d''} \right) \right] + \\[2mm]
& + \left. \left(\frac{1}{x_{qt}''} - \frac{1}{x_{qt}} \right) \left[\frac{(s\tau_q'')^2}{1+(s\tau_q'')^2} - \frac{s\tau_q''}{\sqrt{[1+(s\tau_q'')^2]}} \cos \left(2st - \arctan \frac{1}{s\tau_q''} \right) \right] \right\}
\end{aligned}$$

$$\qquad (2.10)$$

when the regulator is present, E_d is substituted for E_d', and x_{dt}, for x_{dt}'.

In the expression for the reactive power, taken by the generator operating asynchronously, the pulsations are important as well as the mean value, because it is the pulsations which cause the fluctuations of the system voltage.

The load characteristics

When some of the generators of a system operate asynchronously there is no need to take special account of the induction-motor component of the load. The methods already discussed can then be used to determine the effect of the falling voltage on the slip of the motors and the consequent danger of their stalling, or to calculate the effect of changes of frequency.

The equivalent circuit of the transmission lines and of the other system elements need not be altered if the frequency of the system is only slightly affected by the generators operating asynchronously. If the change of frequency is appreciable, the calculation should be refined by increasing the generator voltage, by multiplying inductive reactances by ω/ω_0, and by correspondingly reducing the capacitive reactances. This rule applies to generators with independent excitation. If the generator and the exciter have a common shaft, and the frequency increases, the voltage varies according to the relation $E = E_0\, \omega^n$. However, the calculation, which can only be made by a step-by-step method, becomes so complicated that in practice the simpler method is generally used. Besides, the values of the asynchronous constants in equations (2.7) and (2.10) are only very approximately known, so that a refined calculation is not justified.

During asynchronous operation the losses of active power in the rotor and stator windings, in the damper windings, and in the solid parts of the machine (rotor, metallic wedges, banding wires) have a marked effect on its performance. The effective resistance of the circuits representing these losses does not remain constant but changes considerably with the slip (Fig. 2.3). The change occurs because the frequency of the currents in the rotor windings and other closed circuits increases with increase of slip. There is a pronounced skin effect and the effective resistance rises. The effective leakage reactance also varies with the slip, but to a smaller extent than the resistance. Consequently, all the machine constants vary with the slip, which ini ts turn depends on the operating conditions in the system.

This dependence of the parameters of the machine and of the system on the operating condition makes an exact solution of the equations impossible.

The simplified approach, using formulae (2.2), (2.3), (2.7), and (2.8), gives a broad general insight into the behaviour of the system. Alternatively, a particular process, lasting for a relatively short time, may be

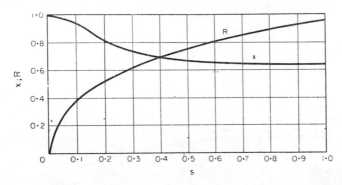

Fig. 2.3. Effective rotor resistance and leakage reactance of a generator as functions of the slip (after I. A. Syromyatnikov).

considered in greater detail. Some examples of such methods are given in the following sections.

2.2. Falling-out of Synchronism and Stable Asynchronous Operation

The process of falling-out of synchronism is discussed by considering the very simple system illustrated in Fig. 2.4. It is assumed that one half of the double transmission line is first opened and is later re-closed, thus returning the system to its normal operating condition. It is also assumed that the shock received by the generator rotor is so great that it accelerates and pulls out of synchronism.

The initial stage of the transient process is analysed by assuming that the value of the slip $s = - \, d\delta/dt$ is very small, and that $T = P$. The equal area criterion, based on the following relation, is then applied:

$$\frac{1}{2} \cdot J \cdot \left(\frac{d\delta}{dt}\right)^2 = \int \Delta T d\delta, \qquad (2.11)$$

where J is the per-unit inertia.[7, 8, 9]

During the transient process the area 3′–4–5 when the machine is braking is smaller than the area 1–2–3–3′ when it is accelerating. Thus the rotor, having passed through the region 4–5 in which it is subject to braking forces, is accelerated again. The acceleration begins at point 5, increases, and becomes appreciable when the load angle reaches 200–300°. With increase of speed (and of slip) the asynchronous torque and the power increase, causing the turbine regulators to reduce the intake of steam or water. This is illustrated in Fig. 2.4, where curve 5–6 shows the change of the turbine torque, and curve 7–7′ shows the increase of the asynchronous torque.

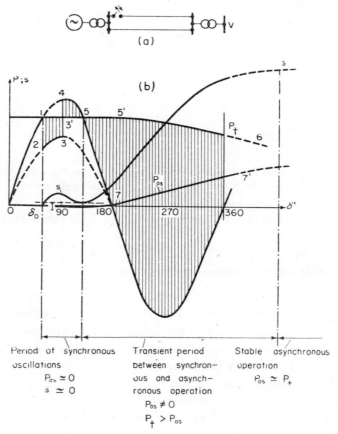

FIG. 2.4. Loss of synchronism of a generator followed by stable asynchronous operation. (*a*) circuit diagram of the system; (*b*) process of losing synchronism.

At a certain value of slip the turbine torque becomes equal to the asynchronous torque, bringing the generator into stable asynchronous operation.

The value of slip s_∞ at which stable asynchronous operation commences can be determined graphically as shown in Fig. 2.5. This method assumes that the relation $T_{as} = f(s)$ is known, and that the relation $T_t = f(s)$ (allowing for the action of the turbine regulator) is linear.

The slip s_∞ and the corresponding asynchronous torque $(T_{as})_\infty$ are the quantities which describe the state of stable asynchronous operation.

It is clear that a full step-by-step calculation, which took account of each interval in the changes of turbine output, the synchronous power, and the asynchronous power, would give a more accurate result.

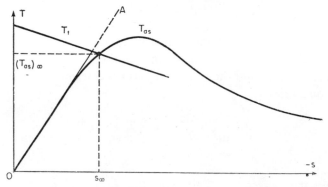

FIG. 2.5. Asynchronous generator torque T_{as} and turbine torque T_t as functions of slip.

Assuming first that the generator is perfectly symmetrical and is un-excited, and hence that the active power supplied by it to the network does not pulsate, the electrical torque corresponding to this power balances the mechanical torque supplied by the turbine. The slip of the generator then has the constant value s_∞. In such conditions the steady-state asynchronous operation of the machine is determined by the characteristics shown in Fig. 2.5.

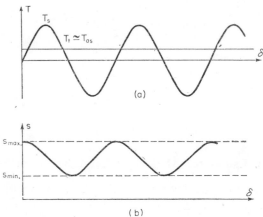

FIG. 2.6. (*a*) Pulsation of synchronous torque T_s; (*b*) slip-pulsation caused by pulsation of T_s.

If, however, the machine is excited, then in addition to the balanced asynchronous torques, its shaft is also subject to a synchronous torque. This torque changes its direction as shown in Fig. 2.6(*a*), and causes the slip to pulsate between the two extremes s_{max} and s_{min} (Fig. 2.6(*b*)).

The amplitude of the pulsation depends on the magnitude of the synchronous component of torque, and the slip has its minimum value at an angle δ close to 180°, if the asynchronous torque and the turbine torque are small. Appreciation of this periodic variation is important in determining the conditions for resynchronization.

The relative motion of the generator rotor is determined by the equation (per-unit quantities)

$$J \cdot \frac{d^2\delta}{dt^2} = T_t - (T_s + T_{as}) = \Sigma T,$$

or, alternatively,

$$J \cdot \frac{ds}{d\delta} \cdot s = \Sigma T, \tag{2.12}$$

where
$$s = -\frac{d\delta}{dt}.$$

If s, T_t, and T_{as} are regarded as functions of δ, then by integration of (2.12)

$$\frac{1}{2} \cdot J \cdot s^2 = \int_{\delta_\infty}^{\delta} \Sigma T \cdot d\delta + C_1,$$

where $C_1 = \frac{1}{2} \cdot J \cdot s_\infty^2$.

The instantaneous value of s is then

$$s = \sqrt{\left(s_\infty^2 + \frac{2}{J} \int_{\delta_\infty}^{\delta} \Sigma T \cdot d\delta \right)}. \tag{2.13}$$

2.3. Equal-area Method at Large Values of Slip

In developing the equal area criterion it is normally assumed that the kinetic energy $\Delta A = \int \Delta P dt$ stored by the rotor in virtue of its relative motion can be written in the form $\Delta A = \int \Delta P d\delta$. This assumption is valid only if the changes of speed caused by the oscillation of the rotor are small. The equal area method needs to be modified if the changes of speed become appreciable compared with the synchronous speed.

It follows directly from equation (2.13) that the equal-area method is valid if the torque is used rather than the power. It is also necessary, when applying the method in any given interval (e.g. from δ_∞ to δ) to take account of the initial slip (in this case s_∞).

It is possible, however, to express the basic relations in terms of the power, as shown below.

The actual change of kinetic energy can be written as

$$\int \Delta P \mathrm{d}t = \frac{1}{2} J_0 [\Omega^2 - \Omega_s^2] = J \cdot \left(\frac{\Delta\omega^2}{2} + \Delta\omega \right)$$

or, by assuming $\omega > \omega_s$, i.e. a negative value of slip corresponding to generator operation,

$$\int \Delta P \mathrm{d}t = J \cdot \left(\frac{s^2}{2} - s \right). \tag{2.14}$$

The equation for the relative motion of the synchronous machine is

$$J \cdot \frac{\mathrm{d}^2\delta}{\mathrm{d}t^2} = J \cdot \frac{\mathrm{d}s}{\mathrm{d}\delta} \cdot s = T_t - (T_s + T_{as}).$$

The excess power of the turbine P_T, i.e. its power output less all the losses, is given by

$$P_T = T_t(1 - s).$$

Allowing for the action of the speed regulator, the turbine torque T_t is a function of the slip

$$T_t = f(s).$$

The synchronous power P_s and the synchronous torque T_s are functions of the angle δ, while the asynchronous power P_{as} is a function of the slip (and of the angle δ for an asymmetrical rotor).

Using per-unit quantities ($P_{as} = T_{as}$), it may be written

$$J \cdot \frac{\mathrm{d}s}{\mathrm{d}\delta} \cdot s = \frac{P_t - P_s}{1 - s} - P_{as}.$$

The instantaneous value of the slip can now be determined from equation (2.13)

Rewriting the above equation

$$J \cdot (1 - s) \cdot s \cdot \mathrm{d}s = [P_t - P_s - P_{as}(1 - s)] \, \mathrm{d}\delta$$

and integrating

$$J \cdot \left(\frac{s^2}{2} - \frac{s^3}{3} \right) + C_1 = - \int_{\delta_\infty}^{\delta} P_s d\delta + \int_{\delta_\infty}^{\delta} [P_t - P_{as}(1-s)] \, d\delta . \qquad (2.15)$$

On assuming the initial value of slip to be s_∞ at $\delta = \delta_\infty$,

$$C_1 = - \left(\frac{s_\infty^2}{2} - \frac{s_\infty^3}{3} \right) \cdot J .$$

It is now possible to obtain the value of $J \cdot \left(\dfrac{s^2}{2} - s \right)$ from equation (2.15)

$$J \left(\frac{s^2}{2} - s \right) = - \int_{\delta_\infty}^{\delta} P_s d\delta + \int_{\delta_\infty}^{\delta} [P_t - P_{as}(1-s)] \, d\delta + F , \qquad (2.16)$$

where

$$F = \left(\frac{s_\infty^2}{2} - \frac{s_\infty^3}{3} + \frac{s^3}{3} - s \right) \cdot J .$$

By writing $P_t - P_{as}(1-s) = \Delta P_{as}$ and using equation (2.15), this equation becomes

$$\Delta A = \int_{\delta_\infty}^{\delta} \Delta P_{as} d\delta - \int_{\delta_\infty}^{\delta} P_s d\delta + F . \qquad (2.17)$$

Equations (2.16) and (2.17) can be regarded as mathematical formulations of the equal area criterion, applied to the condition when the slip is large.

Thus the kinetic energy of the rotor can be represented graphically by three components:

(a) the area proportional to the difference between the turbine power P_t and the product $P_{as}(1-s)$,

(b) the area representing the pulsation of synchronous power,

(c) the quantity F, dependent on the initial and the instantaneous values of slip.

By making the simplifying assumption $P_s = P_m \sin \delta$, equation (2.17) can be rewritten

$$\int \Delta P dt = P_m (\cos \delta_\infty - \cos \delta) + F + \int_{\delta_\infty}^{\delta} \Delta P_{as} \cdot d\delta . \qquad (2.18)$$

If the machine is not excited, $P_m = 0$ and equation (2.18) becomes

$$\int \Delta P dt = F + \int_{\delta_\infty}^{\delta} \Delta P_{as} \cdot d\delta , \qquad (2.19)$$

which can be regarded as the formulation of the equal-area criterion for the special case.

If under this condition the asynchronous operation commences at δ_∞, the mean slip is constant and equal to $-s_\infty$. If it is now assumed that the generator is excited, a slight increase of the excitation brings about an increase in the synchronous torque T_s and causes the slip $(-s)$ to decrease. Hence the values of F and of the asynchronous torque T_{as} also decrease, resulting in a net accelerating torque $\Delta T = T_t - T_{as}$ (Fig. 2.7(a)).

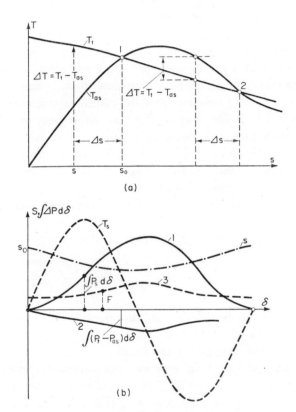

FIG. 2.7. Torque and energy characteristics during asynchronous operation. (*a*) asynchronous and turbine torques as functions of the slip; (*b*) components of energy stored by the moving rotor, (1) due to synchronous torque T_s; (2) due to net accelerating torque ΔT; (3) due to initial velocity; s_0 is the mean slip.

Figure 2.7(*b*) shows graphically the various components of $\int \Delta P dt$, i.e. the increase in kinetic energy. If at some angle $\delta = \delta_1$ the increase in kinetic energy becomes equal to zero, the rotor speed becomes equal to the synchronous speed ($s = 0$) and the machine attains a condition such that it may pull into synchronism.

Mathematically this condition can be expressed by

$$\int_{\delta_\infty}^{\delta} P_s \mathrm{d}\delta + F + \int_{\delta_\infty}^{\delta} [P_t - P_{as}(1-s)] \, \mathrm{d}\delta = 0 . \tag{2.20}$$

2.4. Resynchronization and Self-synchronization of Alternators operating Asynchronously above Synchronous Speed

Resynchronization of an asynchronously operating machine. It has been shown that when a machine, which is operating asynchronously, is excited, the slip pulsates between s_{max} and s_{min}. For some value of the exciting current the slip may pass through zero. A decrease of the power of the prime mover may also cause the slip to pass through zero.

A slip equal to zero indicates that the additional kinetic energy stored by the rotor is also equal to zero, and that the asynchronous component of torque has disappeared, since the generator is at synchronous speed. Whether the generator is able to remain in synchronism depends upon the relation between the electrical power P_s and the turbine power; in other words, on the value of δ at which $s = 0$.

In general, $s = 0$ is a necessary but not a sufficient condition for pulling into synchronism.

It follows from equation (2.13) that $s = 0$ if

$$s_\infty = \sqrt{\left(-\frac{2}{J} \int_{\delta_\infty}^{\delta} \Sigma T \mathrm{d}\delta \right)} .$$

This condition can be satisfied at various values of δ and of the ratio T_s/T_t.

For example, the increase of the exciting current and of the synchronous torque may be such that, with increasing amplitude of the slip oscillation, s_{min} becomes zero ($\mathrm{d}\delta/\mathrm{d}t = 0$) (Fig. 2.8(a)). This instant can be considered as the start of a process of synchronization, although permanent resynchronization may not be achieved.

The process of resynchronization depends on the nature of the relation between the slip and the torque of the turbine. If the torque of the turbine follows the change of asynchronous torque, but lags behind it somewhat (Fig. 2.8(a)), the pulling into synchronism occurs at an angle δ near $(n \times 180)°$, where n is a positive integer. This is followed by an oscillation with an amplitude of nearly 180° (between points 1 and 2 in Fig. 2.8(a)).

If, however, the turbine torque is not zero at $\delta = 180°$, the resynchronization process is unstable. Such a case $(T_t > 0)$ is illustrated by

Fig. 2.8(*b*) in which the area during acceleration exceeds the area during retardation.

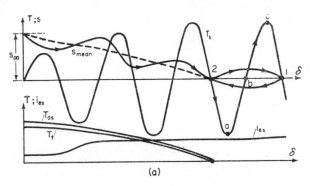

(a)

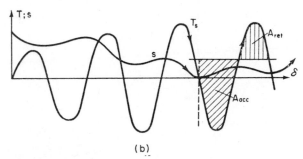

(b)

Fig. 2.8. Resynchronization of a generator brought about by increased excitation. (*a*) attempt successful; (*b*) attempt unsuccessful.

Actually the turbine torque does not decrease with decrease of the mean value of slip, but rather remains constant or increases (Figs. 2.9(*a*) and 2.9(*b*)). The torque changes are determined by the transient characteristic $T_t = f(s)$ which, when the action of the regulator is taken into account, may be quite different from the steady-state characteristic.

With the decreasing slip there appears a torque $\Delta T_t = T_t - T_{as}$ which is opposite in sense to the synchronous torque T_s. The slip, which is determined by the resultant torque $T_{res} = T_s - \Delta T_t$, changes as shown in Figs. 2.9(*c*), 2.9(*d*), and 2.9(*e*). It is clear that the greater the effect of ΔT_t, the larger is the departure from 180° of δ_{syn} (the angle at which the slip passes through zero). This means that synchronous operation commences at a smaller value of δ.

The effect of ΔT_t is the greater the larger, the asynchronous torque and the steeper the slope of the curve $T_t = f(s)$.

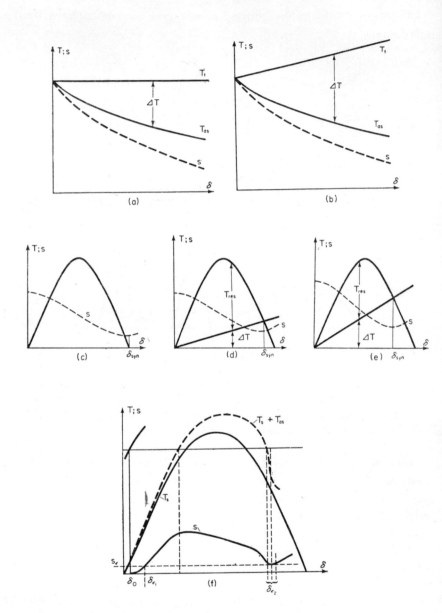

FIG. 2.9. Effect of the turbine output and the asynchronous power of the generator on the conditions of resynchronization. (*a*) variation of ΔT when $T_t = \text{const}$; (*b*) variation of ΔT when T_t increases and s falls; (*c*) synchronization with $\Delta T = 0$, $\delta_{\text{syn}} = 180°$; (*d*) synchronization when ΔT increase as s falls; (*e*) same as (*d*) but with steeper rise of ΔT; synchronization due to T_s and T_{as} only.

On the other hand, the greater the excitation and hence the synchronous torque, the nearer to 180° is the angle δ_{syn} at which synchronous operation commences (Figs. 2.9(c), 2.9(d), and 2.9(e)).

When considering the transition from asynchronous to synchronous operation it will be arbitrarily assumed that the asynchronous component of torque becomes significant only at values of slip s greater than s_ε.

Thus, in Fig. 2.9(f) the asynchronous component of torque is included only at angles between δ_{ε_1} and δ_{ε_2}, and is assumed to be zero when $\delta < \delta_{\varepsilon_1}$ or $\delta > \delta_{\varepsilon_2}$. The total torque $(T_s + T_{as})$ is shown by a thick dotted line.

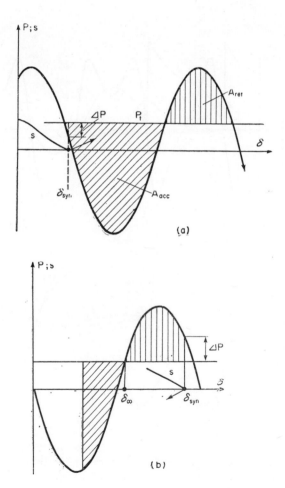

FIG. 2.10. Two attempts at resynchronization. (a) attempt unsuccessful $\delta = \delta_{\text{syn}}$ when $P_t > P_s$; (b) attempt successful $\delta = \delta_{\text{syn}}$ when $P_t < P_s$.

If the generator shaft near synchronous speed is assumed to be subject to only two components of torque, namely the synchronous torque $T_s = P_s = P_m \sin\delta$ and a constant turbine torque $T_t = P_t = \text{const}$, there are two possible conditions when synchronization may be attempted:

$$(a) \quad s = 0 \quad \text{at} \quad P_t > P_s \quad (\text{Fig. 2.10}(a))$$
$$(b) \quad s = 0 \quad \text{at} \quad P_t < P_s \quad (\text{Fig. 2.10}(b)).$$

If the turbine torque and the excitation remained constant, the machine would always fail to synchronize in the first case, but would pull-in in

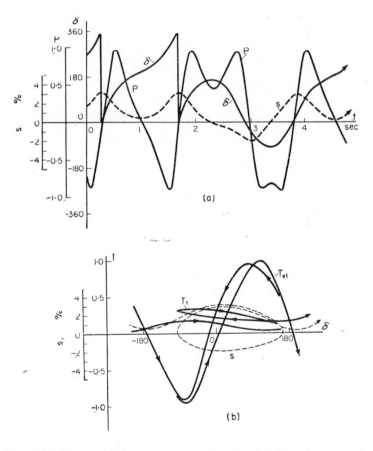

FIG. 2.11. Unsuccessful attempt at synchronization (based on actual oscillograms; case analogous to that in Fig. 2.10(b)), but with changing turbine torque leading to growing amplitude of pulsations following resynchronization. (a) P, δ, s, as functions of time; (b) T_t, T_{el}, s, as functions of load angle δ.

the second. On the other hand, if the torque or the excitation alter while the shaft is oscillating, synchronization may not be achieved even in condition (*b*) (Fig. 2.11).

In the case shown in Fig. 2.10(*a*), the machine may resynchronize if, during the second swing, the excitation is increased and the turbine torque decreased. The increase of excitation would lead, however, to pulsations of longer duration and larger amplitude, during which the machine could easily become unstable and pull out of synchronism (Figs. 2.12(*a*) and

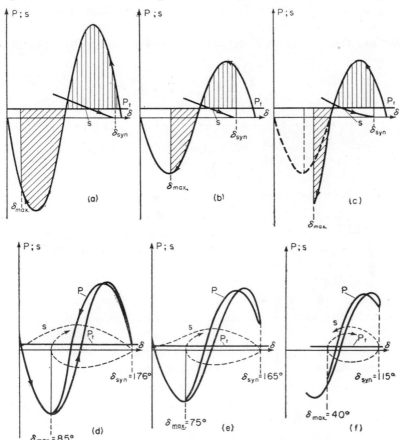

FIG. 2.12. The effect of excitation on the resynchronization process. *a, b, c* — comparison of acceleration and retardation areas. *d, e, f* — *s, P, P_t* as functions of load angle δ.

2.12(*d*)). A decrease of the angle δ_{syn} at which synchronous speed is attained, is, however, always favourable, since the amplitude of the pulsation is thereby decreased (Figs. 2.12(*b*) and 2.12(*e*)).

It is also possible to reduce the amplitude of the pulsations and damp them more rapidly by increasing the exciting current during the second swing (Figs. 2.12(*c*) and 2.12(*f*)).

An examination of the cases considered leads to some important practical conclusions:

(1) When the asynchronous torque is small, e.g. for a generator feeding a long line, it is advantageous to begin synchron zation at a reduced value of exciting current or with the excitation removed. Only when the speed is nearly synchronous ($s = 0$), should the excitation be increased, in order to ensure smooth entry into synchronism without undue pulsation. The synchronous torque T_s is then related to the angle δ and the time as follows:

$$T_s = \frac{EV}{(1-s)\,x}\left(1-\varepsilon^{-\frac{t}{\tau}}\right) \cdot \sin \delta\,.$$

(2) When the asynchronous torque is appreciable, e.g. for a turbo-generator feeding a short line, or a synchronous motor, resynchronization should be attempted with a large value of exciting current. As in the first case a further increase in exciting current after reaching synchronous speed is advantageous, because it reduces the pulsations.

Self-synchronization

Self-synchronization, i.e. synchronization of an unloaded and unexcited machine, presents a problem similar to that of resynchronization. The distinction lies in the fact that for resynchronization the machine is normally excited all the time, while for self-synchronization the machine is excited either at the same time as the switch is closed, or shortly afterwards.

If, during the process of self-synchronization the excitation is applied when the generator speed is somewhat above synchronism, the synchronous torque increases gradually, thus increasing the amplitude of the slip pulsations, and pulling the machine into synchronism whatever the angle δ at which the excitation is introduced.

Figure 2.13(*a*) shows the change of the exciting current and the areas representing acceleration and retardation for a machine running at a speed above synchronism. Figure 2.13(*b*) shows the variation of δ with time. The curves show that, after the excitatioɴ is applied at time $t = 0$, the rotor decelerates due to the synchronous torque, and hence the slip and the asynchronous torque ($T_{as} = P_d \cdot s$) are both reduced, reaching zero at $\delta = \delta_{syn}$. The value of δ continues to increase when the machine is already

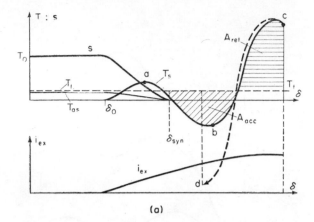

(a)

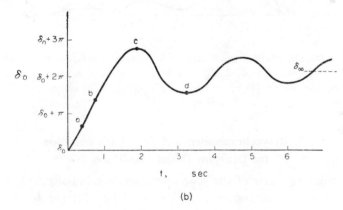

(b)

FIG. 2.13. Self-synchronization of a machine running above synchronism. (a) variation of torque and slip with exciting current; (b) load angle variation during self-synchronization.

in synchronism and is running at a mean value of slip equal to zero. The character of the resulting pulsations is determined by the relation between the retardation and acceleration areas (Fig. 2.13(a)). If the turbine torque and the initial value of slip s_0 are large, the rotor pulsations continue for a considerable time and are of large amplitude. The final angle at which the machine synchronizes may be $(\delta_{syn} + 2\,n\pi)$, i.e. the rotor may pass through two or three complete revolutions before locking into synchronism (Fig. 2.14).

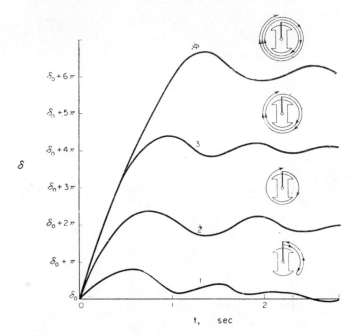

Fig. 2.14. The effect of the initial slip s_0 on synchronization of a generator: $J = 6$ sec, $T_t = 0 \cdot 2$; $\delta_0 = 0$. Machine excited at the instant of
closing the switch (1) $s_0 = -2 \cdot 5\%$; (2) $s_0 = -6\%$; (3) $s_0 = -8\%$;
(4) $s_0 = -11\%$.

2.5. Resynchronization and Self-synchronization
for Different Initial Conditions

Apart from the case of the generator operating initially with negative
slip (speed above synchronous), three other cases deserve to be briefly
mentioned.

(1) *A generator operating below synchronous speed when it is switched
on to the supply.* If the slip is such that the generator, operating as an
asynchronous machine, produces a braking torque on the shaft, this
torque is balanced by the driving torque of the turbine. The synchronous
torque, which appears when excitation is introduced, acts in an
analogous manner to that just described, although it may be either
positive or negative.

(2) *A generator operating initially above synchronous speed with a resultant braking torque* (T_{as} and T_t acting in the same sense). Even if there were
no synchronous torque, the rotor would approach synchronous speed
and the slip would approach zero. However, at the instant when $s = 0$,

the angle δ may have a value such that the synchronous torque causes a further drop in speed, i.e. an increase of slip in the opposite direction.

This effect may be accentuated by the appearance of an additional braking torque, associated with network losses depending on the excitation. As a result, it may happen that the critical slip is passed, and, at the instant when the synchronous torque has the correct sign, the slip is so large and the asynchronous torque so small that the machine does not pull in. For such a case it is possible to speak of a certain "probability of synchronization", of which the value is low when the initial excitation is high.

(3) *A generator operating below synchronous speed, with a resultant accelerating torque* (T_{as} and T_t acting in the same sense). The operation is analogous to case (2). The braking effect due to excitation losses may be beneficial, especially if the value of T_t is large.

The remarks concerning the harmful effect of the excitation on the synchronization process apply only to its initial stages. If the excitation is introduced at the instant of synchronism, or very close to it, the effects of excitation are, as a rule, beneficial.

The process of pulling into synchronism under any condition is determined approximately by the following equation:

$$J \cdot \frac{d^2\delta}{dt^2} = T_t - T_s - T_{as} ,$$

where

$$T_s = \frac{P_s}{1-s} .$$

(For a salient-pole machine P_s is calculated from equation (2.9).)

If the slip is small it is admissible to take $T_s \simeq P_s$. The mean asynchronous torque $T_{as\,(mean)} = f(s)$ is given by equation (2.2b).

The transient variation of the excitation current is determined by the equation

$$(\tau'_d \cdot p + 1) E_d = E_{de} .$$

The solution of these equations with various initial conditions provides a method of determining the angle, the induced voltage, the torque and the current at the instant of synchronizing.

Figure 2.15 illustrates the results obtained by solving these equations for a large synchronous generator. Figures 2.15(*a*) and 2.15(*b*) give the curves for a machine which is connected to the system at $s_0 \simeq -3\%$ and $\delta_0 \simeq 45°$, the excitation being applied at the instant of connexion. The asynchronous torque at this instant happens to be somewhat greater than the mechanical torque, but its braking effect cannot be felt immedia-

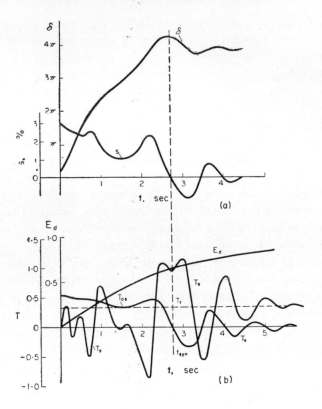

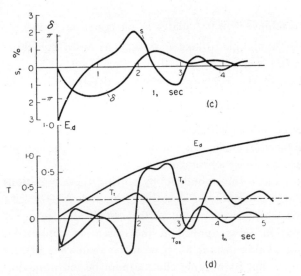

FIG. 2.15. Self-synchronization of a generator: $J = 15$ sec; $T_t = 0.25$: (a) changes of load angle and slip when switching occurs at a speed above synchronism ($s = -3\%$; $\delta = 45°$); (b) variation of T_{as}, T_t, T_s, and E_d for conditions as in (a); (c) changes of load angle and slip when switching occurs at a speed below synchronism ($s \approx +3\%$; $\delta = 0°$); (d) variation of T_{as}, T_t, T_s, and E_d for conditions as in (c).

tely, since the rotor angle continues to change because of the kinetic energy stored by the rotor when rotating at $s = s_0$.

In the earlier analysis of the synchronizing process by the equal-area method, the assumption was made that synchronous operation commenced at $s = 0$, after which the equal-area criterion could be used. The solution of the system of equations just established indicates the correctness of this assumption since, following synchronization, the asynchronous compo-

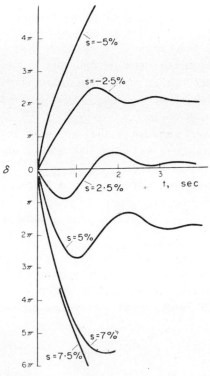

FIG. 2.16. The effect of the initial slip on the resynchronization of a generator, $J = 15$ sec; $T_t = 0 \cdot 2$; $\delta = 0°$.

nent of torque pulsates about a mean value equal to zero and cannot have any appreciable effect on the relative movement of the rotor.

Normally $T_t > 0$, and the process of synchronization at a positive value of slip (speed less than synchronous), when the synchronous and asynchronous components of torque have the same sense, follows the curves shown in Figs. 2.15(*c*) and 2.15(*d*). The effect of the initial slip is illustrated by the curves shown in Fig. 2.16, which relate to a generator connected at $\delta = 0$.

CHAPTER 3

SMALL DISTURBANCES ASSOCIATED WITH SMALL VARIATIONS OF SPEED

3.1. Statement of the Problem

The study of the behaviour of an electrical system subjected to small disturbances from a steady state is important in assessing the operation of the system under normal conditions, particularly when determining its steady-state stability and deciding on the most advantageous method of automatic excitation control.

By the *steady-state stability* of the system is understood its ability to return spontaneously to its initial state after a small disturbance from that state.

A more exact definition can be given as follows:
any system is stable if the magnitude of the deviation due to a disturbance becomes less than a given quantity ε after a sufficiently long interval of time, i.e.

$$\lim_{t \to \infty} \left| \Delta\varphi(t) \right| \leqslant \varepsilon .$$

Consequently the behaviour of any system when subjected to small disturbances (i.e. small enough for the system to be treated as linear) provides a means of assessing its steady-state stability (Fig. 3.1).

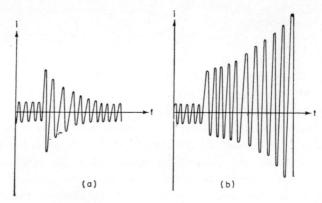

(a)   (b)

FIG. 3.1. Current in a system following a small disturbance.
(*a*) stable system; (*b*) unstable system.

84

A distinction is made between *inherent stability*, and *artificial stability*, i.e. the stability given to an unstable system by automatic control devices.

The problems, which can be studied by considering small changes or small oscillations, are not limited to those concerned with stability. In any power system it is important to ensure very rapid damping of small oscillations occurring during normal operation, and to make quite certain that self-oscillation, i.e. oscillation with increasing amplitude, cannot arise. Such self-oscillation may be called *oscillatory instability* (Fig. 3.2).

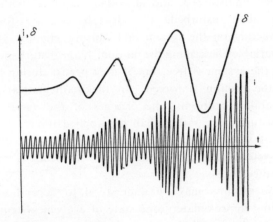

FIG. 3.2. Oscillatory instability in a system (load angle δ and current i).

The method of small oscillations is also essential in checking the operation of the various controlling elements of a power system, for example, the excitation control of the generators, or the governing of the turbines.

Control equipment of proper design should improve not only the stability of the system at increased power, but also its operation under other conditions met in practice. The method of small oscillations can be used to show whether the control of excitation and speed is able to hold the voltage and frequency within the specified limits, while maintaining a satisfactory sharing of the load between the various generator sets.

Thus the method of small oscillations has a wide field of application in studying the behaviour of a complete system, as well as in the design of its separate components.

The stability problem which is of particular interest in the present context can be formulated as follows: a set of differential equations is established, describing the state of a system in motion under the influence of given forces, e.g. the relative motion of an electro-mechanical system.

Following Lyapunov such motion can be called undisturbed. It is now assumed that at a certain instant of time $t = 0$, the system is suddenly acted upon by an additional small force, which disappears after having produced certain small changes $\Delta\delta$, ΔV, ΔP etc. At the instant $t = 0$, these initial deviations bring about a "free motion" or, in other words, a "disturbance". The motion is quite independent of the nature or magnitude of the force, since it has been assumed that the force is very small.

The initial motion of the system, the stability of which is being investigated, is called undisturbed, and all other motions, with which it is compared, are called disturbed. The disturbances are forces (in the general sense) acting on the system and causing changes in the initial values of the variables describing the motion. If the disturbances disappear, the motion of the system is free, but if they persist during the period of investigation, the motion is forced. In the mathematical treatment of steady-state stability problems, the changes of the variables are often taken as the disturbances, rather than the applied forces.

This point of view leads to a concept of steady-state stability as the property of a system to have a "steady state", to which it tends to return after a disturbance.

Alternatively, stability may be understood to depend on the possibility of replacing approximately one state of a given system by another, that is, replacing the actual disturbed state by an idealized undisturbed state.

If this view is adopted, the initial variations of the variables are looked upon not as disturbances but as *errors* (either calculated or observed) in the variables of the equivalent system.

The problem is then not whether the actual condition is stable, but whether the condition which replaces it is realizable.

The above concepts and definitions apply only to the case of small disturbances. Larger disturbances, during which the disturbing forces act continuously and the displacements caused by them are large (so that the non-linearities are important) must be considered under the heading of *transient stability*.

The object of the present discussion is not to determine the magnitude of the changes of the variables or to calculate the function $\delta = f(t)$, but rather to study the character of the motion, and to ascertain whether the system can or cannot return to its initial state without external aid. The stability of the initial steady state is determined by the effect on it of small suddenly applied forces, which do not appear in the differential equations of the system.

A first approximation to a solution of such a problem can be obtained by studying the signs of the roots of the characteristic equation of the system, without solving the differential equation. It is, of course, possible to assume some definite disturbance, rather than a generalized indefinite one, as a cause of the free motion, and to determine its effect on the variables in the system, for example, the angle δ in a synchronous machine. This is, in fact, necessary if complete detail is required, but the problem is then much more complicated. For such a solution it is necessary to decide whether the amplitude of the disturbance is small enough to neglect the non-linearities, or whether a set of non-linear differential equations must be solved.

If the differential equations describing the motion are linear, it is easy o determine whether the motion is stable or not. The solution of the inear differential equation of an oscillatory system has the form

$$x = C_1 \varepsilon^{p_1 t}, + C_2 \varepsilon^{p_2 t}, + \cdots + C_n \varepsilon^{p_n t},$$

where $p_1, p_2, \ldots p_n$ are the roots of the characteristic equation (assumed all to be different) and $C_1, C_2, \ldots C_n$ are constants of integration.

It is clear that if even a single root of the characteristic equation is positive, one of the constituent terms of the unknown quantity increases continuously, and the system is unable to return to its original state. On the other hand, if all the roots are negative, all the terms decay to zero. Imaginary roots indicate undamped oscillations, while complex roots indicate oscillations of varying amplitude, either decreasing or increasing according to the sign of the real part of the root (Figs. 3.3 and 3.4).

When the differential equations are linear, the solution is readily obtained and the problem presents no difficulty. It is important, however, to devise methods of attack for cases where a solution is either impossible or very difficult. These methods are very important, because, for nearly all real practical operative conditions, the differential equations are non-linear.

A number of simplifed methods for obtaining first approximations to a solution have been in use for many years. In general, the equations are linearized by expanding the non-linear terms into a Taylor series and neglecting terms of higher order than the first. When such methods were first used, the justification for such approximations was not well established, since the problem solved differed from the original one, and the connexion between the two problems was not always clear. The first detailed treatment of this question and of many others associated with stability problems was given in a famous paper by A. M. Lyapunov (1892). In this paper the

problem of stability was stated in its most general form and rigorous methods
of solution were provided.

Lyapunov developed his theory of stability for the study of celestial

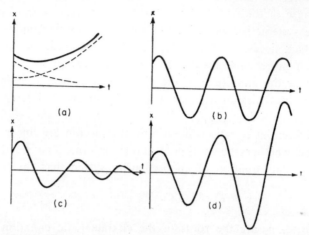

FIG. 3.3. The nature of the transient process in relation to the kind
of roots in the characteristic equation. (a) real roots $(p = \pm\alpha)$;
(b) imaginary roots $(p = \pm j\gamma)$; (c) complex roots with negative real parts
$(p = -\beta \pm j\alpha)$; (d) complex roots with positive real parts $(p = +\beta \pm j\alpha)$.

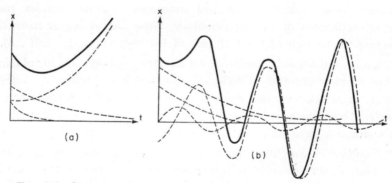

FIG. 3.4. The components of a variable in a complicated system.
(a) all roots of the characteristic equation are real; (b) some roots are
real and some complex.

mechanics, but in recent times it has found wide application in engineering
science and practice, particularly in connexion with rapidly acting and
sensitive automatic control systems.

Lyapunov set himself the task of finding an answer to the following important problem:

"To define the conditions, under which the first approximation definitely settles the question of stability, and to develop methods of solution for at least some of the conditions where the first approximation is inadequate."

Lyapunov was the first to prove rigorously the following two theorems, on which the application of linearized equations to the solution of stability problems is based. They are reproduced here without proof.

(1) If the characteristic equation of a set of linearized differential equations for a disturbed motion has roots with only negative real parts, the undisturbed motion is stable. Any disturbed motion for which the amplitude of disturbance is small must approach the undisturbed motion asymptotically.

(2) If some of the roots of the characteristic equation of the linearized system of differential equations have positive real parts, the undisturbed motion is unstable.

In other words, if, after linearization of the equations of a disturbed motion, all the roots of the corresponding characteristic equation lie on the left half of the complex plane, the undisturbed motion is stable, but if any of the roots fall on to the right half, the undisturbed motion is unstable.

The application of these two theorems cannot give a satisfactory answer in all cases. Thus, for example, if some of the roots lie exactly on the imaginary axis, a more refined analysis is required.

This limitation was pointed out by Lyapunov himself, who suggested some special methods of solution. It is unnecessary to treat of them here, since the two theorems of Lyapunov suffice for most practical problems.

If the method of Lyapunov is applied, there is no need to solve the differential equations of the real system. It is sufficient to determine, by any suitable method, the algebraic sign of the real parts of the roots of the characteristic equation corresponding to the linearized differential equations. Since, in applying this method, the cause of the disturbance is excluded, the internal relations, which determine whether the system is stable, are clearly shown. The problem is thus treated in a much more general way than if a study is made of the behaviour of the system due to a given applied disturbance.

To summarize, the investigation of the behaviour of a system subjected to a small disturbance from a given steady state can be made in two ways:

(a) to discover the internal properties of the system by making a small change in its operational conditions;

(b) to subject the system to a given small disturbance and to determine the time variation of the variables $\Delta\delta$, ΔI_{as}, and ΔV.

3.2.   The Equation of an Unregulated System Subject to Small Disturbances and the Analysis of its Steady-state Stability

The application of the general principles of the theory of stability to electrical power systems will be illustrated by discussing first the simplest example of a single station connected through a network to an infinite system at constant voltage and frequency, and supplying any number of constant impedance loads.

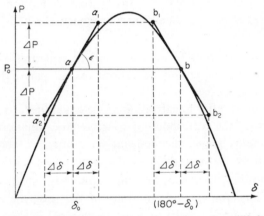

FIG. 3.5. Small deviations from a position of equilibrium.

The relation $P = f(\delta)$ between the power P and the load-angle δ at constant excitation current is constructed for an unregulated system (Fig. 3.5). When considering small changes of δ near the point a it is then possible to make a linear approximation and write for the increment of power ΔP

$$\Delta P = \Delta\delta \cdot \tan\varepsilon .$$

The partial derivative with respect to δ at the point a determines the slope of the line $a_2\, a_1$,

$$\tan\varepsilon = \frac{\partial P}{\partial\delta} .$$

The equation of the free motion for small disturbances (small values of $\Delta\delta$) is then

$$J \cdot \frac{\mathrm{d}^2\Delta\delta}{\mathrm{d}t^2} = -\Delta P = -\Delta\delta \cdot \frac{\partial P}{\partial\delta} ,$$

where J is the inertia coefficient, equal to twice the kinetic energy possessed by the rotor at synchronous speed.* Increments of power causing an increase of δ are considered positive.

If P depends only on the angle δ, then $\dfrac{\partial P}{\partial \delta} = \dfrac{dP}{d\delta} = S_{E_d}$, where S_{E_d} is often called the *synchronizing power coefficient*.

By introducing the differential operator $p = \dfrac{d}{dt}$ and rearranging, the equation of motion becomes

$$J \cdot p^2 \cdot \Delta\delta + S_{E_d} \cdot \Delta\delta = 0 \,.$$

The solution gives the unknown quantity $\Delta\delta$,

$$\Delta\delta = \frac{0}{J \cdot p^2 + S_{E_d}} \,. \tag{3.1}$$

Thus $\Delta\delta$ can differ from zero only if the denominator $J \cdot p^2 + S_{E_d} = 0$. But the solution is indeterminate, making it impossible to obtain the numerical values of $\Delta\delta = f(t)$. This result is not unexpected since, as stated in section 3.1, the problem is to determine the character of the motion independently of the absolute value of the unknown $\Delta\delta$. The denominator of equation (3.1) equated to zero is the characteristic equation of the system, which has two roots

$$P_{1,2} = \pm \sqrt{\left(\frac{-S_{E_d}}{J}\right)} \,.$$

Both roots are imaginary when S_{E_d} is positive, and real when S_{E_d} is negative.

In the first case the motion is given by

$$\Delta\delta = C_1 \varepsilon^{j\gamma t} + C_2 \varepsilon^{-j\gamma t} = C \sin(\gamma t + \psi) = C \sin\left(\frac{2\pi t}{\tau_0} + \psi\right),$$

where

$$\gamma = \sqrt{\frac{S_{Ed}}{J}} \quad \text{or} \quad \tau_0 = 2\pi \sqrt{\frac{J}{S_{Ed}}}$$

---

* *Translators' note*: When the quantities are expressed in "per unit" terms, the inertia coefficient J is twice the "inertia constant" H used in British and American literature.

$$\text{and } C = \sqrt{(C_1^2 + C_2^2)}, \qquad \psi = \arctan \frac{C_2}{C_1}.$$

This equation represents an undamped oscillation and is shown graphically in Fig. 3.6(*a*). In a practical system the oscillation is damped because of the losses, so that the system is stable.

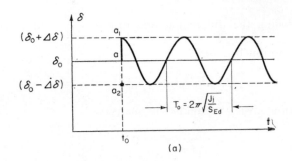

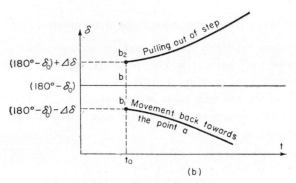

(b)

FIG. 3.6. The nature of the transient process. (*a*) oscillation at the point *a* (Fig. 3.5) caused by a small deviation $\Delta\delta$ from $\delta = \delta_0$; (*b*) changes at the point *b* caused by a small deviation $\Delta\delta$ from $\delta = (180^\circ - \delta_0)$.

In the second case Fig. 3.6(*b*), the equation of motion is $\Delta\delta = C_1\varepsilon^{p_1 t} + C_2\varepsilon^{p_2 t}$.

The term corresponding to the positive root increases continuously, so that the system moves away from its condition of equilibrium. The loss of stability is aperiodic, since there is no oscillation.

When the system is stable, the nature of the oscillation $\Delta\delta = f(t)$ depends on the load at which the generator is operating. The angular frequency γ is proportional to the magnitude of the roots of the characteristic equation, while the periodic time $\tau_0 = 2\pi \sqrt{(J/S_{E_d})}$ is inversely proportional to it.

Consequently, an increase of the load and a decrease of the synchronizing power coefficient S_{E_d} causes an increase in the periodic time τ_0. In the limit, when $P = P_{max}$, τ_0 becomes infinite. The loss of stability is very slow and is aperiodic.

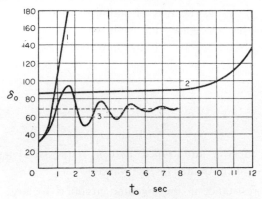

FIG. 3.7. Comparison of two examples of loss of stability and of a damped oscillation.

(1) loss of transient stability, $d\delta/dt$ of the order 200–500 el.deg/sec;
(2) loss of steady-state stability, $d\delta/dt$ of the order 0·5–1 el.deg/sec;
(3) oscillation, $d\delta/dt$ of the order 150–200 el. deg/sec.

It should be specially noted that in this case the loss of stability occurs at $P = P_{max}$. The time-rate of change of the angle δ in the initial stages does not exceed 1 to 2 electrical degrees per second. This state of affairs is very different from that occurring when transient stability is lost at very much higher values of $d\delta/dt$ (Fig. 3.7).

If the damping torque is taken into account, the equation of motion can be written

$$J \cdot p^2 \Delta \delta + P_d \cdot p \Delta \delta + S_{E_d} \Delta \delta = 0 . \tag{3.2}$$

The corresponding characteristic equation is then

$$J \cdot p^2 + P_d \cdot p + S_{E_d} = 0 .$$

The roots of this equation are:

$$p_{1,2} = \frac{-P_d \pm \sqrt{(P_d^2 - 4JS_{E_d})}}{2J} = \pm \sqrt{\left\{ -\left[\frac{S_{Ed}}{J} - \left(\frac{P_d}{2J} \right)^2 \right] \right\}} - \frac{P_d}{2J} .$$

The presence of the negative real part indicates that the oscillation is damped under the influence of the damping torque. The frequency of self-oscillation is reduced by an amount depending on the damping effect.

In this case again the roots $p_{1,2}$ can have positive real parts only when $S_{E_d} < 0$. Consequently, any unregulated machine remains stable when $S_{E_d} > 0$.

If the resistances in the machine circuit are so low that it is admissible to take $P = P_{max} \cdot \sin \delta$, the loss of stability occurs at the critical value of $\delta = 90°$. If the resistances are somewhat greater the critical angle increases to $(90° + \alpha)$, where α is the impedance angle. If the resistance is so large that $\alpha \geqslant \delta_0$, the effect may be of the opposite kind. For now it is possible to write

$$P = E^2 y \sin \alpha - EVy \sin (\alpha - \delta) ,$$

and

$$S_{E_d} = -EV \cos (\alpha - \delta_0) ,$$

where y is the effective admittance, and δ_0 is the steady-state angle. In deriving S_{E_d}, $(\alpha - \delta)$ is treated as the variable.

Thus, if the resistance in the machine circuit is so large that δ_0 is less than α, the system can lose stability long before the load angle reaches $90°$; instability can occur if the condition $\delta_0 \leqslant \alpha$ is satisfied.

The frequently observed instability of small machines with appreciable stator resistance, as well as instability of large machines at light loads (δ_0 small), are to a considerable extent due to the causes just discussed, though in reality the process is more complex and the instability is oscillatory in character.

To take account of the changes of electromagnetic transient processes:

$$Jp^2 \Delta\delta + \Delta P = 0; \quad \Delta E_d + \tau_{do} p \Delta E'_d = 0$$

$$\Delta P = S_{E_d} \Delta\delta + P'_{E_d} \Delta E_d, \text{ or}$$

$$\Delta P = S'_{E_d} \Delta\delta + P'_{E'_d} \Delta E'_d,$$

where

$$S'_{E_d} = \frac{\partial P_{E'_d}}{\partial \delta}; \quad P'_{E_d} = \frac{\partial P_{E_d}}{\partial E_d}; \quad P'_{E'_d} = \frac{\partial P_{E'_d}}{\partial E'_d}.$$

The characteristic equation of this system is:

$$J\tau'_d p^3 + Jp^2 + S'_{E_d} p + S_{E_d} = 0.$$

The Routh-Hurwitz criteria of stability are then:

$$\tau'_d > 0; \quad S'_{E_d} > 0; \quad S_{E_d} > 0; \quad S'_{E_d} - S_{E_d} > 0.$$

The stability of the system may be lost if $S_{E_d} \leqslant 0$ (as in the case just considered) or under two conditions of *self-maintained oscillation*:

(a) $\tau'_d = \dfrac{x'_d - x_L}{x_d - x_L} \cdot \tau_{do} < 0$; this may happen if $x_L > x'_d$, $x_L < x_d$, and x_L is negative (lines with series capacitors, or capacitive loading);

(b) $S_{E_d} - S'_{E_d} \leqslant 0$; this may occur under light load conditions when the stator resistance is appreciable (δ small and α large).

In this discussion it has been assumed that the power delivered by the turbine is not affected by the change of the machine speed $\Delta\omega$. Such an assumption is justified as long as the speed changes are small and occur in a machine of finite power connected to an infinite bus.

To take account of the changes of the driving torque of the turbine and of the electromagnetic torque of the generator which occur when the speed changes, it is necessary to introduce the incremental torque ΔT instead of the incremental power ΔP into the differential equation. ΔT is the difference between the increments of the mechanical and electromagnetic torques

$$\Delta T = \Delta T_{\text{mech}} - \Delta T_{\text{el}} .$$

The increment of mechanical torque depends on the change of speed, while the increment of electromagnetic torque is a function of two variables—the changes of speed and angle,

$$\Delta T_{\text{mech}} = \varphi(\Delta\omega) = \frac{\partial T_{\text{mech}}}{\partial\omega} \cdot \Delta\omega$$

$$\Delta T_{\text{el}} = \frac{\partial T_{\text{el}}}{\partial\omega} \cdot \Delta\omega + \frac{\partial T_{\text{el}}}{\partial\delta} \cdot \Delta\delta .$$

If $\Delta\omega$ is replaced by $\dfrac{d\Delta\delta}{dt}$ and $\dfrac{d\omega}{dt}$ by $\dfrac{d^2\Delta\delta}{dt^2}$, the final equation of motion has the form:

$$J \cdot \frac{d^2\Delta\delta}{dt^2} + \left(\frac{\partial T_{\text{el}}}{\partial\omega} - \frac{\partial T_{\text{mech}}}{\partial\omega} \right) \frac{d\Delta\delta}{dt} + \frac{\partial T_{\text{el}}}{\partial\delta} \cdot \Delta\delta = 0 .$$

The roots of the characteristic equation are:

$$p_{1,2} = - \frac{1}{2J} \left(\frac{\partial T_{\text{el}}}{\partial\omega} - \frac{\partial T_{\text{mech}}}{\partial\omega} \right) \pm$$

$$\pm \sqrt{\left[\frac{1}{4J^2} \left(\frac{\partial T_{\text{el}}}{\partial\omega} - \frac{\partial T_{\text{mech}}}{\partial\omega} \right)^2 - \frac{1}{J} \cdot \frac{\partial T_{\text{el}}}{\partial\delta} \right]} .$$

From this it follows that the operation is stable if

$$\left(\frac{\partial T_{\text{el}}}{\partial\omega} - \frac{\partial T_{\text{mech}}}{\partial\omega} \right) \geqslant 0 , \quad \text{and} \quad \frac{\partial T_{\text{el}}}{\partial\delta} > 0 .$$

Thus, if the effect of changes of speed is taken into account, the additional condition to be satisfied in order to ensure stability is as follows:

$$\frac{\partial(T_{\text{el}}-T_{\text{mech}})}{\partial\omega}\geqslant 0 . \tag{3.3}$$

In practice this additional condition is automatically satisfied by systems without control, or under control by conventional regulators. In these cases the electromagnetic torque always increases with increase of frequency, so that its rate of change is always positive, while the mechanical torque (supplied by the prime mover) decreases with increase of speed (i.e. of frequency), and has a negative rate of change. Hence the stability condition (3.3) is always satified.

When, however, forced regulation is used, controlled by the first and the second derivatives of the angle, and the speed is governed at the same time, the combined action of the regulators can lead to a condition when $\partial T_{\text{el}}/\partial\omega < \partial T_{\text{mech}}/\partial\omega$. The real parts of the roots then become positive, and the amplitude of self-oscillation increases.

When a system of greater complexity is considered, containing two or more stations of finite output, it becomes necessary to distinguish absolute displacements (relative to the synchronous axis) ($\Delta\delta_1$, $\Delta\delta_2$, etc.) the time rates of which determine the mechanical accelerations, and the relative displacements ($\Delta\delta_{1,2} = \Delta\delta_1 - \Delta\delta_2$, etc.) which determine the electrical power delivered by the generators.

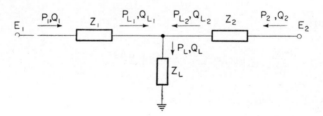

FIG. 3.8. System diagram.

With two stations connected as shown in Fig. 3.8, the differential equations are of the form:

$$J_1 \cdot p^2\Delta\delta_1 + S_1\Delta\delta_{12} = 0 ; \quad J_2 \cdot p^2\Delta\delta_2 + S_2\Delta\delta_{12} = 0$$

or

$$p^2\Delta\delta_1 + \frac{S_1}{J_1}\Delta\delta_{12} = 0 ; \quad p^2\Delta\delta_2 + \frac{S_2}{J_2}\Delta\delta_{12} = 0 .$$

These two equations can be combined by subtracting the second from the first

$$p^2 \Delta \delta_{12} + \left[\frac{1}{J_1} S_1 - \frac{1}{J_2} S_2 \right] \Delta \delta_{12} = 0 .$$

If the concept of relative acceleration a_{12} is now introduced

$$a_{12} = \frac{1}{J_1} S_1 - \frac{1}{J_2} S_2 = \frac{1}{J_1} \cdot \frac{dP_1}{d\delta_{12}} - \frac{1}{J_2} \cdot \frac{dP_2}{d\delta_{12}} .$$

The characteristic equation of the system becomes $p^2 + a_{12} = 0$, and its two roots

$$p_{1,2} = \pm j\sqrt{a_{12}} .$$

The criterion of stability is thus a positive value of a_{12}. For the system with two stations, it clearly depends on the magnitudes of their respective inertia constants.

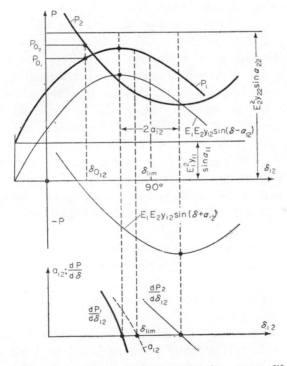

FIG. 3.9. Power $P = f(\delta_{12})$, relative acceleration $a_{12} = f(\delta_{12})$, and synchronizing power coefficient $dP/d\delta$ as functions of the relative displacement angle δ_{12}.

Here a new factor is encountered, namely, the effect of inertia on the steady-state stability of the system. It is of considerable practical significance that the power limit of the first station supplying the load is now no longer the same as the stability limit of the transmission line, as it was in the case considered earlier.

In order to emphasize this point, the characteristics of the two stations are drawn in Fig. 3.9. If the total load is assumed to remain constant, an increase in the power delivered by the first station corresponds to a reduction of the power supplied by the second station, as shown by the curves P_1 and P_2 in Fig. 3.9.

$$P_1 = E_1^2 y_{11} \sin \alpha_{11} + E_1 E_2 y_{12} \sin (\delta_{12} - \alpha_{12})$$

$$P_2 = E_2^2 y_{22} \sin \alpha_{22} - E_1 E_2 y_{12} \sin (\delta_{12} + \alpha_{12}). \tag{3.4}$$

In systems of the type shown in Fig. 3.8, the sign of α_{12} (the angle of the transfer impedance) is usually negative. Since in the first of the formulae (3.4) the symbol α_{12} enters with a negative sign, the characteristic P_1 has a maximum at $\delta_{12} = (90° - \alpha_{12})$, while the characteristic P_2 passes through a minimum when $\delta_{12} = (90° + \alpha_{12})$. Thus the maximum and the minimum points of the two characteristics are separated by an angle $2\alpha_{12}$.

The synchronizing power coefficients $dP_1/d\delta_{12}$ and $dP_2/d\delta_{12}$ also pass through zero at two different values of δ_{12}, separated by the same angle $2\alpha_{12}$ (Fig. 3.9). The characteristic representing the relative acceleration $a_{12} = f(\delta_{12})$ lies between the curves of the two synchronizing powers, as shown in Fig. 3.9. It is evident that the relative acceleration must always pass through zero at a larger angle δ_{12} than that at which P_1 has its maximum. Thus, for the system containing two stations, the limit of stability $a_{12} = 0$ always occurs at an angle larger than that at which the power limit is reached. If the power of the second station is increased, the two limits approach each other, and when the second station is replaced by an infinite bus they coincide. On the other hand, the smaller the inertia of the second station, the closer to $2\alpha_{12}$ is the angle separating the point of maximum power and the stability limit.

The practical significance of this analysis lies in the fact that the system consisting of two stations is capable of operating at the point of maximum power without loss of stability when subjected to small disturbances. It should be pointed out, however, that normally the angle α_{12} is small, and the angular separation between the point of maximum power and the stability limit seldom exceeds 5–10°.

If the load has to be represented by a set of static characteristics rather than by a constant impedance, as is done above, the qualitative nature of the problem is not affected, but its detailed solution becomes much more complicated.

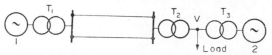

FIG. 3.10. Diagrams of a 2-station system.

When applied to the solution of the system shown in Fig. 3.10 it is assumed that the steady magnitudes of E_1, E_2, V, δ_1 and δ_2 are known. The expressions for the active and reactive power components of the two stations and of the load are as follows:

$$
\left.
\begin{aligned}
P_1 &= E_1^2 y_{11} \sin \alpha_{11} + E_1 V y_{l_1} \sin (\delta_1 - \alpha_{l_1}) \\
Q_1 &= E_1^2 y_{11} \cos \alpha_{11} - E_1 V y_{l_1} \cos (\delta_1 - \alpha_{l_1}) \\
P_{L_1} &= -V^2 y_{l_1} \sin \alpha_{l_1} + E_1 V y_{l_1} \sin (\delta_1 + \alpha_{l_1}) \\
Q_{L_1} &= -V^2 y_{l_1} \cos \alpha_{l_1} + E_1 V y_{l_1} \cos (\delta_1 + \alpha_{l_1}) \\
P_2 &= E_2^2 y_{22} \sin \alpha_{22} + E_2 V y_{l_2} \sin (\delta_2 - \alpha_{l_2}) \\
Q_2 &= E_2^2 y_{22} \cos \alpha_{22} - E_2 V y_{l_2} \cos (\delta_2 - \alpha_{l_2})
\end{aligned}
\right\}
\quad (3.5)
$$

Since from (3.5) $P = f(\delta, V)$, it follows that

$$
dP_1 = \frac{\partial P_1}{\partial \delta_1} \cdot d\delta_1 + \frac{\partial P_1}{\partial V} \cdot dV.
$$

The synchronizing power coefficients are given by:

$$
\left.
\begin{aligned}
\frac{dP_1}{d\delta_{12}} &= \frac{\partial P_1}{\partial \delta_1} \cdot \frac{d\delta_1}{d\delta_{12}} + \frac{\partial P_1}{\partial V} \cdot \frac{dV}{d\delta_{12}} \\
\frac{dP_2}{d\delta_{12}} &= \frac{\partial P_2}{\partial \delta_2} \cdot \frac{d\delta_2}{d\delta_{12}} + \frac{\partial P_2}{\partial V} \cdot \frac{dV}{d\delta_{12}}
\end{aligned}
\right\}
\quad (3.6)
$$

The partical derivatives $\dfrac{\partial P_1}{\partial \delta_1}$, $\dfrac{\partial P_1}{\partial V}$, $\dfrac{\partial P_2}{\partial \delta_2}$, $\dfrac{\partial P_2}{\partial V}$ are obtained by differentiation of (3.5). Differentiation of P_1 yields:

$$
\frac{\partial P_1}{\partial \delta_1} = E_1 V y_{l_1} \cos (\delta_1 - \alpha_{l_1}) \quad \text{and} \quad \frac{\partial P_1}{\partial V} = E_1 y_{l_1} \sin (\delta_1 - \alpha_{l_1}).
$$

The derivatives $\dfrac{d\delta_1}{d\delta_{12}}$, $\dfrac{d\delta_2}{d\delta_{12}}$ and $\dfrac{dV}{d\delta_{12}}$ can be obtained from equations for the power components at the point at which the load is connected.

Thus, $P_{L_1} + P_{L_2} = P_L$ and $Q_{L_1} + Q_{L_2} = Q_L$,   or

$$dP_{L_1} + dP_{L_2} = dP_L \quad \text{and} \quad dQ_{L_1} + dQ_{L_2} = dQ_L.$$

In these expressions $P_L = f(\delta, V)$ and $Q_L = \varphi(\delta, V)$. Hence,

$$dP_{L_1} = \frac{\partial P_{L_1}}{\partial \delta_1} \cdot d\delta_1 + \frac{\partial P_{L_1}}{\partial V} \cdot dV; \quad dP_{L_2} = \frac{\partial P_{L_2}}{\partial \delta_2} \cdot d\delta_2 + \frac{\partial P_{L_2}}{\partial V} \cdot dV$$

$$dQ_{L_1} = \frac{\partial Q_{L_1}}{\partial \delta_1} \cdot d\delta_1 + \frac{\partial Q_{L_1}}{\partial V} \cdot dV; \quad dQ_{L_2} = \frac{\partial Q_{L_2}}{\partial \delta_2} \cdot d\delta_2 + \frac{\partial Q_{L_2}}{\partial V} \cdot dV$$

and

$$dP_L = \frac{dP_L}{dV} \cdot dV; \quad dQ_L = \frac{dQ_L}{dV} \cdot dV.$$

When these relations are substituted into the power equations, the latter take the form:

$$\frac{\partial P_{L_1}}{\partial \delta_1} \cdot d\delta_1 + \frac{\partial P_{L_2}}{\partial \delta_2} \cdot d\delta_2 + \left(\frac{\partial P_{L_1}}{\partial V} + \frac{\partial P_{L_2}}{\partial V} - \frac{dP_L}{dV} \right) \cdot dV = 0$$

and

$$\frac{\partial Q_{L_1}}{\partial \delta_1} \cdot d\delta_1 + \frac{\partial Q_{L_2}}{\partial \delta_2} \cdot d\delta_2 + \left(\frac{\partial Q_{L_1}}{\partial V} + \frac{\partial Q_{L_2}}{\partial V} - \frac{dQ_L}{dV} \right) \cdot dV = 0.$$

Since, however, $\delta_1 - \delta_2 = \delta_{12}$, $d\delta_2 = d\delta_1 - d\delta_{12}$, the following relations hold:

$$\left(\frac{\partial P_{L_1}}{\partial \delta_1} + \frac{\partial P_{L_2}}{\partial \delta_2} \right) \cdot d\delta_1 + \left(\frac{\partial P_{L_1}}{\partial V} + \frac{\partial P_{L_2}}{\partial V} - \frac{dP_L}{dV} \right) \cdot dV = \frac{\partial P_{L_2}}{\partial \delta_2} \cdot d\delta_{12}$$

$$\left(\frac{\partial Q_{L_1}}{\partial \delta_1} + \frac{\partial Q_{L_2}}{\partial \delta_2} \right) \cdot d\delta_1 + \left(\frac{\partial Q_{L_1}}{\partial V} + \frac{\partial Q_{L_2}}{\partial V} - \frac{dQ_L}{dV} \right) \cdot dV = \frac{\partial Q_{L_2}}{\partial \delta_2} \cdot d\delta_{12}$$

or

$$A_P \cdot \frac{d\delta_1}{d\delta_{12}} + B_P \cdot \frac{dV}{d\delta_{12}} = \frac{\partial P_{L_2}}{\partial \delta_2}$$

and

$$A_Q \cdot \frac{d\delta_1}{d\delta_{12}} + B_Q \cdot \frac{dV}{d\delta_{12}} = \frac{\partial Q_{L_2}}{\partial \delta_2}$$

$$\left. \vphantom{\begin{array}{c} a \\ a \\ a \\ a \end{array}} \right\} , \qquad (3.7)$$

where,

$$A_P = \frac{\partial P_{L_1}}{\partial \delta_1} + \frac{\partial P_{L_2}}{\partial \delta_2} \; ; \qquad B_P = \frac{\partial P_{L_1}}{\partial V} + \frac{\partial P_{L_2}}{\partial V} - \frac{dP_L}{dV} \; ;$$

$$A_Q = \frac{\partial Q_{L_1}}{\partial \delta_1} + \frac{\partial Q_{L_2}}{\partial \delta_2} \; ; \qquad B_Q = \frac{\partial Q_{L_1}}{\partial V} + \frac{\partial Q_{L_2}}{\partial V} - \frac{dQ_L}{dV} \; .$$

Solving Equations (3.7),

$$\left. \begin{aligned} \frac{d\delta_1}{d\delta_{12}} &= \frac{\dfrac{\partial P_{L_2}}{\partial \delta_2} \cdot B_Q - \dfrac{\partial Q_{L_2}}{\partial \delta_2} \cdot B_P}{A_P B_Q - B_P A_Q} \\[4mm] \frac{dV}{d\delta_{12}} &= \frac{\dfrac{\partial Q_{L_2}}{\partial \delta_2} \cdot A_P - \dfrac{\partial P_{L_2}}{\partial \delta_2} \cdot A_Q}{A_P B_Q - B_P A_Q} \end{aligned} \right\} \qquad (3.8)$$

The derivative $d\delta_2/d\delta_{12}$ is obtained from the relation

$$\frac{d\delta_1}{d\delta_{12}} - \frac{d\delta_2}{d\delta_{12}} = \frac{d\delta_{12}}{d\delta_{12}} = 1 \; .$$

Knowing the values of derivatives in equations (3.6) it is easy to calculate the synchronizing power coefficients $dP_1/d\delta_{12}$ and $dP_2/d\delta_{12}$, from which the value of the relative asceleration a_{12} is readily computed

$$a_{12} = \frac{1}{J_1} \cdot \frac{dP_1}{d\delta_{12}} - \frac{1}{J_2} \cdot \frac{dP_2}{d\delta_{12}} \; .$$

3.3. Analysis of the Characteristic Equation by the Method of Separation of Domains

The well-known Routh–Hurwitz criteria are often used to assess the steady-state stability of a system from its equations. Other methods, for example, that due to Mikhailov, are based on the concept of frequency response.

Another method of analysis, proposed and developed by the Soviet scientists, U. I. Neimark, A. A. Sokolov and others, is explained below. This method not only determines the conditions of stability of a system, but also shows how to select the values of the parameters in order to obtain the best results. When the effect of varying a single parameter on the stability of the system is studied, the method is referred to as "domain separation in the plane of a single parameter". If two parameters are considered, the separation of domains is said to take place in a "two-parameter plane".

In this discussion the outline of the method is indicated; for further details the reader is referred to the literature.[10, 11, 12, 13, 14]

Domain separation in the plane of a single parameter can be illustrated by considering the characteristic equation

$$a_0 p^n + a_1 p^{n-1} + \ldots + a_{n-1} p + a_n = 0 \,. \tag{3.9}$$

If it is assumed that this equation contains terms in a single linear parameter $q = a + jb$, taken as complex for the sake of generality, equation (3.9) can be put into the form

$$A_1(p) + q A_2(p) = 0 \,,$$

from which

$$q = -\frac{A_1(p)}{A_2(p)} \,. \tag{3.10}$$

By substituting $j\omega$ for p and separating the real and the imaginary terms

$$q = P(\omega) + jQ(\omega) \,. \tag{3.11}$$

The parameter q can then be represented on a plane with P and Q axes.

If ω takes all values from $-\infty$ to $+\infty$, the corresponding values of $P(\omega)$ and $Q(\omega)$ can be found and the locus of all points satisfying equation (3.9) can be plotted in the q-plane.

This locus forms a boundary dividing the q-plane into domains within which equation (3.9) is satisfied by roots with positive or negative real parts, corresponding respectively to stable and unstable operation of the system.

The following rule due to Neimark determines which of the two domains represents stable operation:

When p traverses the imaginary axis in the p-plane from $-\infty$ to $+\infty$ (Fig. 3.11(*a*)), the corresponding movement of q along the locus in the q-plane leaves the stable domain on the left-hand side (Fig. 3.11(*b*)).

The convention is adopted that the stable domain is indicated by shading the left-hand side of the locus boundary (Fig. 3.11(*b*)).

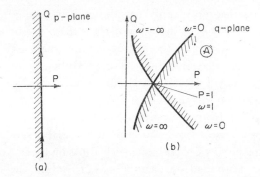

FIG. 3.11. Example of application of the method of separation of domains.

If q changes so that the locus in the q-plane is crossed from the un-shaded to the shaded side, one of the roots in the p-plane leaves the right half-plane by crossing the imaginary axis to the left (Fig. 3.12).

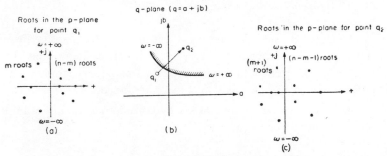

FIG. 3.12. Change of root distribution when the domain boundary is crossed.

Since only real values of q are of practical significance, interest is restricted to the domain separation along the real axis in the q-plane.

The following sequence of steps is used to construct the locus in the q-plane for a single parameter.

(1) The characteristic equation is transformed to express the parameter q explicitly (equation (3.10)).

(2) After substituting $p = j\omega$, the real and imaginary parts of q are separated and the resultant equation is written in the form of equation (3.11).

(3) The locus of q in the q-plane is constructed, with P and Q as co-ordinates, allowing ω to take all values between $-\infty$ and $+\infty$.

(4) Traversing the q-locus in the direction from $\omega = -\infty$ towards $\omega = +\infty$, the left-hand side of the locus is shaded.

The following theorems apply for the case of a single parameter:

(1) If to some point q_1 lying in the q-plane there can be assigned a polynomial with m roots lying to the left of the imaginary axis in the p-plane, then a polynomial corresponding to every other point in the q-plane, which may be reached from q_1 without crossing the locus, also has m roots to the left of the imaginary axis.

(2) If, in moving from the point q_1 in the q-plane to some other point q_2, the locus is crossed from the unshaded to the shaded domain, the polynomial corresponding to q_2 has $(m+1)$ roots on the left of the imaginary axis if the locus is shaded once, and $(m+2)$ roots if the locus is shaded twice.

(3) If the polynomial corresponding to the point q_1 has m roots to the left of the imaginary axis, and if another point q_2 is reached after crossing the locus z times, z_1 crossings being from the shaded to the unshaded domain, and z_2 crossings in the reverse direction, then the polynomial assigned to the point q_2 has $(m+z_2-z_1)$ roots to the left of the imaginary axis.

Consequently, if the distribution of roots relative to the imaginary axis is known for any arbitrary value of q, it can be determined for any other value of q. Hence the appropriate domain corresponding to any particular point on the real axis may be determined.

The use of these rules is illustrated by considering as an example the following characteristic equation:

$$p^3 + qp^2 + p + 1 = 0 .$$

Then

$$q = - \frac{p^3 + p + 1}{p^2} .$$

Substituting $p = j\omega$,

$$q = \frac{j\omega^3 - j\omega - 1}{-\omega^2} = \frac{1}{\omega^2} + j\left(\frac{1}{\omega} - \omega\right) .$$

By giving ω values from $-\infty$ to $+\infty$ the locus of q, shown in part in Fig. 3.11(b), can be constructed.

The polynomials with the largest number of roots to the left of the imaginary axis correspond to the domain designated by A in Fig. 3.11(b). This is true because, in order to reach any point in another domain, the locus must be crossed from the shaded to the unshaded side.

Hence all such points must correspond to polynomials with a smaller number of roots to the left of the imaginary axis than the points within A.

In the present example it is convenient to determine the number of roots of the polynomial corresponding to $q = 1$. The characteristic equation for this value of q reduces to

$$p^3 + p^2 + p + 1 = (p^2 + 1)(p + 1) = 0 .$$

Its roots are:

$$p_1 = -1 ; \qquad p_{2,3} = \pm j .$$

Thus, at $q = 1$, one root lies to the left of the imaginary axis, the remaining two being on it.

In going from the point $q = 1$ to any point within the region A, the movement is into the shaded domain. Since two separate branches of the locus pass through the point $q = 1$, this point lies in a *doubly shaded* area, and any point within A, must have all three roots with negative real parts. Consequently A corresponds to the region of stability.

Domain separation in the plane of two parameters which are linearly separable

Not infrequently the variation of two parameters must be taken into account. Such a problem arises, for example, when the stability of a power system with forced excitation control is investigated. It is then necessary to rewrite the characteristic equation $D(p) = 0$ in such a manner that the two parameters in question k_1 and k_2 are expressed explicitly.

The characteristic equation is written first in the form

$$D(p) = k_2 Q(p) + k_1 N(p) + R(p) = 0 ,$$

where $Q(p)$, $N(p)$, and $R(p)$ are polynomials in p.

Substituting $p = j\omega$ and equating the real and imaginary terms separately to zero, two equations are obtained:

$$\left. \begin{array}{l} k_2 Q_1(\omega) + k_1 N_1(\omega) + R_1(\omega) = 0 \\[2mm] k_2 Q_2(\omega) + k_1 N_2(\omega) + R_2(\omega) = 0 \end{array} \right\} , \qquad (3.12)$$

where

$$Q(j\omega) = Q_1(\omega) + j Q_2(\omega)$$
$$N(j\omega) = N_1(\omega) + j N_2(\omega)$$
$$R(j\omega) = R_1(\omega) + j R_2(\omega) .$$

For any value of ω

$$k_1 = \frac{\Delta_{k1}}{\Delta},$$

and

$$k_2 = \frac{\Delta_{k2}}{\Delta},$$

where Δ is the principal determinant of the system,

$$\Delta = \begin{vmatrix} Q_1(\omega) & N_1(\omega) \\ Q_2(\omega) & N_2(\omega) \end{vmatrix}.$$

The principal determinant Δ is written in such a manner that the coefficients of the parameter to be plotted along the horizontal axis appear in the first column. For present purposes the k_2-axis is chosen to be horizontal, and the k_1-axis vertical (Fig. 3.13).

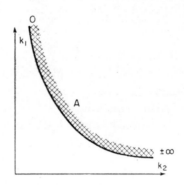

Fig. 3.13. Domain separation in the plane of two parameters.

$$\Delta_{k1} = \begin{vmatrix} Q_1(\omega) & -R_1(\omega) \\ Q_2(\omega) & -R_2(\omega) \end{vmatrix},$$

and

$$\Delta_{k2} = \begin{vmatrix} -R_1(\omega) & N_1(\omega) \\ -R_2(\omega) & N_2(\omega) \end{vmatrix}.$$

If the principal determinant is not equal to zero, a point in the k_1, k_2-plane can be assigned to each value of ω. If ω is allowed to vary continuously from $-\infty$ to $+\infty$, the locus of points so determined forms a corresponding boundary between domains.

The side of the boundary to be shaded is determined by the algebraic sign of the principal determinant. When ω increases from $-\infty$ to $+\infty$, the locus is shaded on the left-hand side if $\Delta > 0$ and on the right-hand side if $\Delta < 0$.

Since the boundary drawn for negative values of ω coalesces with that for positive values of ω $[\Delta(-\omega) = \Delta(\omega)]$, the same side of the boundary is shaded twice.

As ω changes, the algebraic sign of the principal determinant may also change. Two cases can arise when $\Delta = 0$.

(1) The numerators Δk_1 and Δk_2 are finite and not equal to zero. For this case k_1 and k_2 are both infinite, so that Δ vanishes at a point infinitely removed from the domain boundary.

(2) The numerators Δk_1 and Δk_2 are equal to zero. This implies that the equations (3.12) are not independent and that $k_1 = \varphi(k_2)$.

The method of separation of domains is sometimes very laborious in detail. A number of special simplified methods have been described in the literature of the subject.

As an example, the following characteristic equation may be considered:

$$p^3 + k_1 p^2 + k_2 p + 1 = 0 .$$

With $p = j\omega$, the equation becomes

$$-k_1\omega^2 + k_2 j\omega + (1 - j\omega^3) = 0 ,$$

or

$$-k_1\omega^2 + 1 + j(k_2\omega - \omega^3) = 0 ,$$

whence

$$k_1(-\omega^2) + k_2(0) + 1 = 0 ,$$

and

$$k_1(0) + k_2(\omega) - \omega^3 = 0 .$$

The principal determinant of this system

$$\Delta = \begin{vmatrix} 0 & -\omega^2 \\ \omega & 0 \end{vmatrix} = +\omega^3$$

can only vanish if $\omega = 0$.

For any other value of ω

$$k_1 = \frac{1}{\omega^2} ,$$

and

$$k_2 = \omega^2 ,$$

so that

$$k_1 = \frac{1}{k_2} .$$

Thus the locus separating the domains in the k_1, k_2-plane is a rectangular hyperbola.

The point $\omega = 0$ lies at infinity on the k_1-axis, while the points $\omega = +\infty$ and $\omega = -\infty$ lie at infinity on the k_2-axis. The algebraic sign of Δ changes at $\omega = 0$. Hence the double shading of the boundary shown in Fig. 3.13.

The movement across a boundary with double shading corresponds to a change of the algebraic sign of the real part of two conjugate roots of the characteristic equation.

At $k_1 = k_2 = 1$, the equation has one root to the left of the imaginary axis and two roots to the right. Hence the domain A (Fig. 3.13) corresponds to stable operation.

Domain separation when the two parameters are not linearly separable

The method of attack is illustrated by considering a single special case.

Suppose that the parameters in question are T_n and T_k, and that the equation is of the form

$$(1+T_n p)(1+T_k p) \cdot P(p) + k = 0 ,$$

or

$$[1+(T_n+T_k)p + T_n T_k p^2] \cdot P(p) + k = 0 .$$

If now

$$T_n T_k = a \quad \text{and} \quad (T_n+T_k) = b ,$$

$$(a p^2 + b p + 1) \cdot P(p) + k = 0 .$$

When $p = j\omega$,

$$(-a\omega^2 + bj\omega + 1) \cdot P(p) + k = 0$$

or

$$(-a\omega^2 + bj\omega + 1)[P_1(\omega) + jP_2(\omega)] + k = 0 .$$

Separating the real and imaginary parts,

$$\left.\begin{aligned}
(1-a\omega^2)P_1(\omega) - b\omega P_2(\omega) + k &= 0 \\
(1-a\omega^2)P_2(\omega) + b\omega P_1(\omega) &= 0
\end{aligned}\right\} ,$$

whence

$$a = \frac{1}{\omega^2}\left[1 + \frac{kP_1(\omega)}{P_1^2(\omega) + P_2^2(\omega)}\right],$$

and

$$b = \frac{1}{\omega}\left[-\frac{kP_2(\omega)}{P_1^2(\omega) + P_2^2(\omega)}\right].$$

The separation locus is now constructed with a and b as co-ordinates: The determinant Δ is:

$$\Delta = \begin{vmatrix} -P_1(\omega)\omega^2 & -\omega P_2(\omega) \\ \\ -P_2(\omega)\omega^2 & \omega P_1(\omega) \end{vmatrix}$$

$$= -\omega^3 P_1^2(\omega) - \omega^3 P_2^2(\omega) = -\omega^3[P_1^2(\omega) + P_2^2(\omega)].$$

After establishing in the a, b-plane the domain corresponding to the stable region, it is necessary to check whether the values of $a = T_n \cdot T_k$ and $b = (T_n + T_k)$ calculated from the actual values of T_n and T_k lie in this domain.

3.4. Analysis of the Steady-state Stability of a Simple Regulator System by the Method of Small Oscillations

The effect of automatic regulation on the steady-state stability of a system

It has been shown in Section 1.2 that the generator performance may be considerably modified by the action of an automatic regulator. If the regulator is ideal, i.e. instantaneous in its response, the generator can be replaced by some voltage E_x behind an impedance Δx, instead of the voltage E_d behind x_d. The magnitude of Δx becomes the smaller, the more strongly the excitation is forced, i.e. the greater the extent to which the regulator is able to maintain a constant voltage when the load changes. It is possible in practice to attain such a measure of control that either the voltage V_g at the generator terminals, or the voltage V_1, at the sending end of the line is maintained constant. If the regulator response were instantaneous, the calculations for controlled systems (including their steady-state stability and their behaviour when subject to small disturbances) would not differ in principle from those on unregulated systems, since the only effect would be the reduction of the internal impedance of the generator. Since, however, all automatic excitation regulators used in practice possess a certain time delay, it becomes necessary to analyse a controlled system by considering simultaneously the behaviour of the system and of the regulator, in order to arrive at a satisfactory criterion for their combined operation.

Qualitative analysis of a system containing generators with controlled excitation

The characteristics of controlled generators with $E_d = $ const, $V_g = $ const, etc., were constructed in Section 1.2 on the assumption that the induced voltage $\dot{E}_d$ follows accurately any change of load on the generator. It will

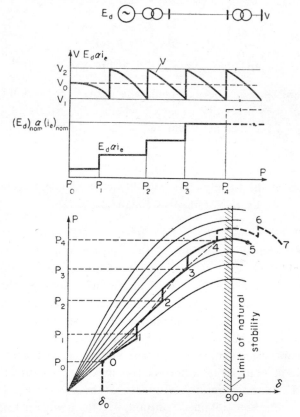

FIG. 3.14. Characteristics of a regulator having a dead zone.

now be assumed that the excitation is controlled by a regulator with a dead zone, usually caused by back-lash in the mechanical parts. A regulator of this type does not respond to changes of voltage smaller than a certain threshold value.

A dead zone is also present with manual control of excitation when an operator observing an indicating instrument (say a voltmeter) cannot sense changes of deflection smaller than a certain value. The presence of time lag in the regulator, in the exciter winding, and in the field circuit of the controlled machine leads to a further slowing down of the response, which is not dissimilar in its effect to that of a dead zone.

In the example shown in Fig. 3.14 it is assumed that when the load changes from P_0 to P_1, the voltage falls from V_0 to V_1. The excitation control remains inoperative, since its threshold of response is defined by the magnitude $\Delta V = V_0 - V_1$. As soon as the voltage reaches the value V_1, the control mechanism immediately increases the exciting current and increases the induced voltage E_d, if there is no time-lag. The operating point is therefore shifted from the characteristic drawn for $E_{d_1} = \text{const}$ to that corresponding to $E_{d_2} = \text{const}$, and so on. The resultant operational characteristic is thus given by the broken line 0–1–2–3–4.

For a control system with a dead zone which is also subject to time-lag, the operational characteristic is continuous, as shown by the dotted line in Fig. 3.14.

In a system for which $E_d = \text{const}$ under all operational conditions and at all values of angle δ, the stability is governed by the condition $S_{E_d} = dP_{E_d}/d\delta > 0$. In such a system the power and stability limits correspond to each other.

For the system illustrated in Fig. 3.14 (which is purely reactive) the limiting value of the angle δ is 90°, beyond which the machine pulls out of synchronism, although with a certain delay, due to the raising of the exciting current by the action of the regulator.

If the action of the regulator is sufficiently rapid it may happen that the machine remains in synchronism. With δ greater than the limiting value, a quasi-stationary state may become established, characterized by large sustained oscillations. This self-oscillation may attain a constant amplitude and remain stable, or lead to instability by increasing in amplitude (Fig. 3.15, (*a*), (*b*)).

The oscillatory process can be explained roughly by using the equal area method.

The point 5 in Fig. 3.14 represents a condition of operation outside the stable region. Figure 3.15 (*c*) shows to a larger scale the relevant portion of Fig. 3.15 (*a*). The terminal voltage of the generator is assumed to be equal to its nominal value at the point 5. When the rotor moves so as to increase the angle δ, the terminal voltage falls, but the regulator does not respond until the change of voltage becomes greater than the threshold value at the point *5'*. From this point onwards the excitation current begins to rise bringing the operating point along the characteristic $P = f(\delta)$ progressively to points *6*, *7* etc. (Fig. 3.15(*c*)).

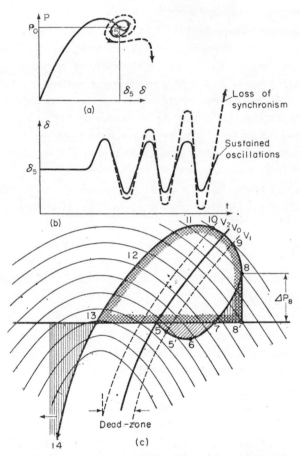

FIG. 3.15. Operation beyond the limit of natural stability with a regulator having a dead zone. (*a*) $P = f(\delta)$; (*b*) $\delta = f(t)$; (*c*) power balance under conditions of sustained oscillation; area 5-6-7-5 = area 7-8'-8-7; area 8'-8-9-10-11-13 = area 13-14 etc.

If the rise of exciting current is sufficiently rapid, the process of falling-out of synchronism is halted at the point *7* where the electrical power and the mechanical power become equal. Nevertheless the rotor cannot remain at that point, for in its motion from point *5* to point *7*, due to the excess of power $\Delta P = P_0 - P_1$, it has stored kinetic energy $\int_{\delta_5}^{\delta_7} \Delta P d\delta$ (measured by the area *5-6-7-5*).

This kinetic energy causes the rotor to maintain its motion to point *8*, at which the gain in kinetic energy is balanced by the energy used in retarding the rotor (measured by the area *7-8-8'-7*).

Between the points *7* and *8* the voltage $V > V_1$, the exciting current continues to rise, shifting the operational point of the machine to other characteristics, corresponding to higher values of the induced voltage.

At the point *8* the increase of angle is arrested, since all of the kinetic energy gained by accelerating the rotor has been used up in providing the braking effect.

Stable operation cannot, however, be maintained at this point, since the electrical power is in excess of the mechanical power.

The lack of balance causes a further drop in speed, accompanied by a further increase in excitation until point *9* is reached. Between *9* and *10* the excitation of the machine remains constant (within the dead zone of the regulator), while from point *10* to point *13* the excitation decreases, indicated by the shift of the operating point to characteristics drawn for lower values of E_d.

By continuing this argument it is easily shown that the operation beyond the point *13* must lead to an increase of amplitude during the next half-cycle. A further increase of amplitude leads to a state of oscillatory instability.

If, however, the generator had an adequate amount of damping, which introduced a power component $P_d \cdot d\delta/dt$ while the speed was rising, the amplitude of oscillation would become stable. (The power component may be due to damper windings on the generator or to special control devices which increase the excitation in proportion to the speed.) In this case the curve $P = f(\delta)$ closes on itself, as shown by the solid line in Fig. 3.15(a).

Operation with oscillations of constant amplitude, though stable, is unacceptable in practice, because of the fluctuations of voltage and current. In other words, a generator with a regulator having a dead zone cannot be operated in the zone of "artificial stability" when $dP_{E_d}/d\delta < 0$.

A further conclusion can be drawn from this analysis, namely, that the narrower the dead zone of the regulator the smaller the amplitude of oscillations when $dP_{E_d}/d\delta > 0$. When a regulator has no dead zone, a higher power output without oscillation can be achieved in the region of operation which is normally unstable. But in this case also, when operating far from the limit of stability (especially when the characteristics $P = f(\delta)$ are steep), the delay present in the regulator elements can lead to oscillation. To overcome this it is necessary to increase the damping, or to introduce another control producing an effect equivalent to damping.

This description of the general behaviour of quick-response regulators can only yield qualitative indications of the desirable features in their design. Broadly speaking, it is desirable that a regulator should have no dead zone, and that the regulating system should have provision for controlled delay depending on various operating quantities (e.g. the speed), so as to damp the self-oscillation in the most effective manner.

To obtain quantitative criteria it is necessary to carry out a detailed mathematical analysis of the regulated system. It should be emphasized, however, before embarking on such an analysis, that the use of quick-response regulators with large gain may lead to self-oscillation even at relatively light loads in the normally stable region.

When excitation is controlled by a regulator without a dead zone, the general equation of motion of the rotor (3.2) can be rewritten as

$$Jp^2 \cdot \Delta\delta + P_d p \cdot \Delta\delta + \frac{\partial P}{\partial \delta} \cdot \Delta\delta + \frac{\partial P}{\partial E} \cdot \Delta E = 0 \,.$$

It is assumed that the system is in oscillation and that the angle varies according to the relation

$$\Delta\delta = \Delta\delta_m \sin \gamma t \,,$$

where γ is the angular frequency of oscillation.

It is further assumed that the changes of induced voltage ΔE follow the changes of angle with a certain delay (Fig. 3.16(a))

$$\Delta E = \Delta E_m \sin (\gamma t - \psi) \,.$$

This can be rewritten as follows:

$$\Delta E = \Delta E_m (\sin \gamma t \cdot \cos \psi - \cos \gamma t \cdot \sin \psi)$$

$$= \Delta E_m \left[\sin \gamma t \cdot \cos \psi - p \cdot (\sin \gamma t) \cdot \frac{1}{\gamma} \sin \psi \right]$$

$$= k_1 \Delta\delta - k_2 p \cdot \Delta\delta \,.$$

The general equation of motion now takes the form

$$Jp^2 \cdot \Delta\delta + P_d p \cdot \Delta\delta + \frac{\partial P}{\partial \delta} \cdot \Delta\delta + k_1 \frac{\partial P}{\partial E} \cdot \Delta\delta - k_2 \frac{\partial P}{\partial E} p \cdot \Delta\delta = 0 \,.$$

The roots of this equation are:

$$p_{1,2} = \pm \sqrt{\left\{ -\frac{1}{J}\left[\frac{\partial P}{\partial \delta} + k_1 \frac{\partial P}{\partial E} \right] + \frac{1}{4J^2}\left(P_d - k_2 \frac{\partial P}{\partial E} \right)^2 \right\}} - \frac{P_d - k_2 \cdot \partial P/\partial E}{2J} .$$

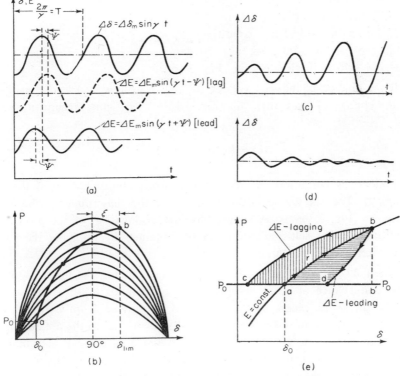

(a)

(b)

(c)

(d)

(e)

Fig. 3.16. The building-up of an oscillation when operating with large values of gain.

It is obvious that when $\partial P/\partial E$ is positive, i.e. when an increase of voltage is associated with an increase of power, the stability region is extended. Without the control with $k_1 = 0$ and $k_2 = 0$ the stability limit is reached when $\delta = 90°$, since $\partial P/\partial \delta = (EV/x) \cos \delta$ becomes negative when $\delta > 90°$. When a regulator is used, the operation remains stable so long as

$$\left(\frac{\partial P}{\partial \delta} + k_1 \frac{\partial P}{\partial E} \right) > 0$$

or

$$\frac{EV}{x} \cos \delta + k_1 \frac{V}{x} \sin \delta = \frac{EV \cos(\delta - \xi)}{x \cos \xi} > 0,$$

where $\xi = \arctan \dfrac{E}{k_1}$.

Consequently the stability region is extended and stable operation is possible up to $\delta = (90° + \xi)$ (Fig. 3.16(b)).

If, however, under any conditions $P_d < k_2 \cdot \partial P / \partial E$, the system loses stability before $\delta = 90°$, because the damping coefficient becomes negative, and self-oscillation occurs (Fig. 3.16(c)).

If the change of induced voltage $\Delta E = \Delta E_m \sin(\gamma t + \psi)$ leads in phase on the change of load angle $\Delta \delta$ (Fig. 3.16(a)), the same argument shows that

$$\Delta E = k_1 \Delta \delta + k_2 p \cdot \Delta \delta.$$

Under this condition the regulator assists stability by improving the damping. The stabilizing effect depends on the magnitude of the coefficient k_2 (Fig. 3.16(d)). A simple physical explanation of the growth of amplitude during self-oscillation can be obtained by applying the equal area criterion (Fig. 3.16(e)).

When ΔE lags behind $\Delta \delta$, the rotor, after reaching the point b due to some disturbance at a, moves back towards c and, in so doing, stores kinetic energy in excess of that acquired in moving from a to b. The energy acquired in moving from a to b is proportional to the area a-b-b'-a, while the excess energy is proportional to the area a-b-c-a. The kinetic energy of the rotor is increased by virtue of the energy supplied from the external sources, i.e. from the network or the turbine.

On the other hand, if the change of voltage is ahead of the change of angle, the movement of the rotor from b to d is associated with a decrease of kinetic energy. The decrease is proportional to the area a-b-d-a.

In the first case (gain in kinetic energy and oscillation with increasing amplitude), the oscillatory process is described by passing round the curve $P = f(\delta)$ (abc) in a counter-clockwise direction. In the second case (damped oscillation), the curve $P = f(\delta)$ (abd) is traversed in a clockwise direction. This graphical interpretation of the change of rotor energy is very instructive.

Analytical expression for the power characterisic of an automatically controlled generator

So far the treatment of the automatically controlled generator has been confined to cases with arbitrary values of gain.

In particular in Section 1.2 special cases were considered in which small changes in the operational conditions were accompanied by changes of exciting current such that the flux linkages with the exciting winding remained constant ($E'_d \simeq E' = \text{const}$), or such that the terminal voltage V_g remained constant.

In the present section two further cases of a much more general nature are considered. The two basic types of control of the induced voltage of the generator are governed by the following relations:

(A) $E_d = E_{d0} + k_I(I - I_0)$ (current-actuated control),

(B) $E_d = E_{d0} + k_V(V_0 - V_g)$ (voltage-actuated control).

In the first case the characteristics $P = f(\delta)$ and $Q = f(\delta)$ can be deduced as follows. The current is first obtained from the triangular vector diagram of the generator.

$$I\sqrt{3} = \frac{\sqrt{(E_d^2 - 2E_d \cdot V \cdot \cos \delta + V^2)}}{x_d}.$$

If now the value for E_d is substituted from (A), the generator current I is obtained by solving the resulting expression,

$$I\sqrt{3} = \frac{1}{x_d^2 - k_I^2} \{\sqrt{[(x_d^2 - k_I^2) \cdot V^2 \cdot \sin^2 \delta + x_d^2 \cdot (E_{d0} - k_I I_0 - V \cdot \cos \delta)^2]} +$$

$$+ k_I(E_{d0} - k_I I_0 - V \cdot \cos \delta)\}.$$

Here E_{d0} and I_0 are the values of voltage and current at which the compounding effect commences.

If the above value of I is substituted back into (A), the relation between E_d and δ is obtained:

$$E_d = \frac{k_I\sqrt{[(x_d^2 - k_I^2)V^2 \cdot \sin^2\delta + x_d^2(E_{d0} - k_I I_0 - V \cos \delta)^2]}}{x_d^2 - k_I^2} +$$

$$+ \frac{x_d^2(E_{d0} - k_I I_0) - k_I^2 V \cdot \cos \delta}{x_d^2 - k_I^2}.$$

It is easy now to calculate the active and reactive components of the power of the controlled generator by substituting this value of E_d into the well-known expressions

$$P = \frac{E_d \cdot V}{x_d} \cdot \sin \delta$$

$$Q = \frac{E_d \cdot V}{x_d} \cdot \cos \delta - \frac{V^2}{x_d}.$$

When the machine is "flat compounded", i.e. when the compounding maintains constant voltage between open circuit and nominal full load, (voltage E_{dn} and current I_n), the compounding ratio k_n is equal to

$$k_n = \frac{E_{dn} - V}{I_n}.$$

In this case the relation between the induced voltage of the machine and the stator current is given by

$$E_{dn} = V + k_n I_n$$

and the expressions for the voltage, the current and the active and reactive power components are:

$$E_d = \left[1 + 2k_n \cdot \sin \frac{\delta}{2} \cdot \frac{\sqrt{(x_d^2 - k_n^2 \cdot \cos^2 \delta/2) + k_n \cdot \sin \delta/2}}{x_d^2 - k_n^2} \right] \cdot V$$

$$\sqrt{3}I = 2V \cdot \sin \frac{\delta}{2} \cdot \frac{\sqrt{(x_d^2 - k_n^2 \cdot \cos^2 \delta/2) + k_n \cdot \sin \delta/2}}{x_d^2 k_n^2}$$

$$P = \left[1 + 2k_n \cdot \sin \frac{\delta}{2} \cdot \frac{\sqrt{(x_d^2 - k_n^2 \cdot \cos^2 \delta/2) + k_n \cdot \sin \delta/_-}}{x_d^2 - k_n^2} \right] \frac{V^2}{x_d} \cdot \sin\delta$$

$$Q = \left[1 + 2k_n \cdot \sin \frac{\delta}{2} \cdot \frac{\sqrt{(x_d^2 - k_n^2 \cdot \cos^2 \delta/2) + k_n \cdot \sin \delta/2}}{x_d^2 - k_n^2} \right] \frac{V^2}{x_d} \cdot \cos \delta - \frac{V^2}{x_d}.$$

$$(3.13)$$

The relations (3.13) apply to a generator feeding directly into an infinite bus of voltage V.

When the generator is connected to such a bus by a line of reactance x_s, the reactance x_d in the above relations is replaced by $x_{dt} = x_d + x_s$. For a complicated network equations (3.13) must be modified by introducing the transfer reactance x_{12}.

Figure 3.17(a) shows graphically the relations $P = f(\delta)$ and $Q = f(\delta)$ according to equations (3.13).

When the generator control is voltage-actuated, i.e. when $E_d = E_{d0} + +k_V \ (V_0 - V_g)$ or, in other words, when $\Delta E_d = -k_V \cdot \Delta V_g$, the vector diagram may be used in a similar manner. An argument analogous to that used for the current-actuated control leads to expressions for the voltage of the generator, the current, and the active component of power in terms of δ, k_V, and the constants of the system. The expression for the power has the form[15]:

$$P = \frac{V \cdot \sin \delta}{x_{dt}(A^2 k_V^2 - 1)} \{\sqrt{(C^2 - (k_V^2 A^2 - 1) [k_V^2 V^2 (1 - A)^2 - B^2])} - C - B\}, \quad (3.14)$$

where

$$A = \frac{x_L}{x_l}; \quad B = E_{d0} + k_V V_0;$$

$$C = V \cdot k_V^2 \cdot A(1 - A) \cos \delta .$$

Equation (3.14) is not exact and is applicable only as a first approximation.

By giving values to A it is possible to construct curves of $P = f(\delta)$ for different values of gain k_V and E_{d0}. These, when analysed, lead to the following approximate rule for a semi-analytical construction of the curves $P = f(\delta)$ for different values of gain.

To construct the characteristics $P = f(\delta)$ for a generator with controlled excitation at different values of gain k_V, the first step is to draw the characteristics $P = f(\delta)$ for $E_d' = $ const, and $V_g = $ const. The maxima of these two curves are then joined by a straight line, divided into six equal segments as shown in Fig. 3.17 (b). Through each of the dividing points on the straight line there passes a characteristic corresponding to a certain value of gain.

The values of gain k_V associated with the dividing points are given by the series 5, 7, 12, 20, 50. The gain k_V associated with the characteristic $V_g = $ const has a value from 80 to 100.

This method, though approximate, is very useful both as an aid to analysis and in the solution of practical problems.

Automatic excitation control, neglecting delays due to the regulator and exciter

The first case to be considered is that of a single station feeding into an infinite system through a pure reactance. It is assumed that damping is negligible and further that the electromagnetic inertia of all the elements of the control system can be neglected in comparison with that of the exciting winding of the generator.

This last assumption is bound to affect the validity of the conclusions reached, and the analysis is of value as an illustration of the method rather than as a practical procedure.

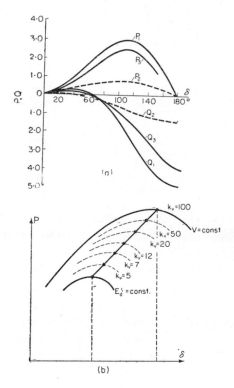

FIG. 3.17. The characteristics $P = f(\delta)$ for a system with generators controlled by regulators without dead zone. (*a*) with compounding, P_1, Q_1 for $x_s = 0$; P_2, Q_2 for $x_s = 1\cdot2$ and $k_n = 0.78$; P_3, Q_3 for $x_s = 1\cdot2$ and $k_n = 0.50$; (*b*) with electronic regulator at various values of gain k_V.

The basic electro-mechanical equation of the generator is

$$J \cdot p^2 \cdot \Delta\delta + \Delta P = 0 . \tag{3.15}$$

If the regulator responds to changes of voltage and if there are no delays in the regulator and the exciter, then the current $(i_f)_{de}$ forced through the exciting winding of the generator, and the induced voltage E_{de} proportional to it, depend directly on the change of the terminal voltage

$$(\Delta i_f)_{de} \propto \Delta E_{de} = -k_V \Delta V_g . \tag{3.16}$$

To simplify matters it is now assumed that ΔV_g is equal to its direct axis component ΔV_{gd}, so that

$$\Delta E_{de} = -k_V \cdot \Delta V_{gd} . \tag{3.17}$$

If this relation is substituted into the equation describing the internal conditions in the generator

$$p\Delta E'_d = \frac{\Delta E_{de} - \Delta E_d}{\tau'_{do}} ,$$

then

$$p\Delta E'_d = \frac{-k_V \cdot \Delta V_{gd} - \Delta E_d}{\tau'_{do}} ,$$

or

$$\Delta E_d = -\tau'_{do} \cdot p\Delta E'_d - k_V \Delta V_{gd} . \tag{3.18}$$

Equations (3.15) and (3.18) express relations between electro-mechanical and electromagnetic quantities. They contain 5 unknowns ($\Delta\delta$, ΔP, ΔE_d, ΔV_{gd}, $\Delta E'_d$). Three additional equations can be obtained by considering the increments of power, as δ changes, in terms of E_d, E'_d, and V_{gd}.

$$\left.
\begin{aligned}
\Delta P &= \frac{\partial P_{E_d}}{\partial E_d} \cdot \Delta E_d + \frac{\partial P_{E_d}}{\partial \delta} \cdot \Delta\delta && = P'_{E_d} \cdot \Delta E_d + S_{E_d} \cdot \Delta\delta \\[2mm]
\Delta P &= \frac{\partial P_{E'_d}}{\partial E'_d} \cdot \Delta E'_d + \frac{\partial P_{E'_d}}{\partial \delta} \cdot \Delta\delta && = P'_{E'_d} \cdot \Delta E'_d + S_{E'_d} \cdot \Delta\delta \\[2mm]
\Delta P &= \frac{\partial P_{V_{gd}}}{\partial V_{gd}} \cdot \Delta V_{gd} + \frac{\partial P_{V_{gd}}}{\partial \delta} \cdot \Delta\delta && = P'_{V_{gd}} \cdot \Delta V_{gd} + S_{V_{gd}} \cdot \Delta\delta
\end{aligned}
\right\} \cdot \text{(3.19)}$$

The coefficients P' and S depend on the operating conditions of the system and have the following values:

$$P'_{E_d} = \frac{\partial P_{E_d}}{\partial E_d} = \frac{V}{x_{dt}} \sin\delta ; \quad S_{E_d} = \frac{\partial P_{E_d}}{\partial \delta} = \frac{E_d \cdot V}{x_{dt}} \cos\delta$$

$$P'_{E'_d} = \frac{\partial P_{E'_d}}{\partial E'_d} = \frac{V}{x'_{dt}} \sin\delta ;$$

$$S_{E'_d} = \frac{\partial P_{E'_d}}{\partial \delta} = \frac{E'_d \cdot V}{x'_{dt}} \cdot \cos\delta - V^2 \cdot \frac{(x_d - x'_d)}{x_{dt} \cdot x'_{dt}} \cdot \cos 2\delta$$

$$P'_{V_{gd}} = \frac{\partial P_{V_{gd}}}{\partial V_{gd}} = \frac{V}{x_L} \sin\delta ;$$

$$S_{V_{gd}} = \frac{\partial P_{V_{gd}}}{\partial \delta} = \frac{V_g \cdot V}{x_L} \cdot \cos \delta - V^2 \cdot \frac{(x_{dt} - x_L)}{x_{dt} \cdot x_L} \cdot \cos 2\delta$$

(where x_L is the external line reactance).

The system of five equations (3.15), (3.18), and (3.19) can be reduced to three by substituting into equations (3.19) ΔP from equation (3.15) and ΔE_d from equation (3.18).

These, when simplified, become:

$$\left. \begin{array}{l} J \cdot p^2 \cdot \Delta \delta - P_{E_d}'(k_V \cdot \Delta V_{gd} + \tau_{do}' \cdot p \cdot \Delta E_d') + S_{E_d} \cdot \Delta \delta = 0 \\[2mm] J \cdot p^2 \cdot \Delta \delta + P_{E_d}' \cdot \Delta E_d' + S_{E_d'} \cdot \Delta \delta \qquad\qquad = 0 \\[2mm] J \cdot p^2 \cdot \Delta \delta + P_{V_{gd}}' \cdot \Delta V_{gd} + S_{V_{gd}} \cdot \Delta \delta \qquad\qquad = 0 \end{array} \right\}.$$

or

$$\left. \begin{array}{l} (J \cdot p^2 + S_{E_d}) \, \Delta \delta - \tau_{do}' \cdot P_{E_d}' \cdot p \cdot \Delta E_d' - P_{E_d}' \cdot k_V \cdot \Delta V_{gd} = 0 \\[2mm] (J \cdot p^2 + S_{E_d'}) \, \Delta \delta + P_{E_d}' \cdot \Delta E_d' \qquad\quad + 0 \qquad\qquad = 0 \\[2mm] (J \cdot p^2 + S_{V_{gd}}) \, \Delta \delta + 0 \qquad\qquad\quad + P_{V_{gd}}' \cdot \Delta V_{gd} = 0 \end{array} \right\}. \quad (3.20)$$

The system of equations (3.20) is homogeneous, since it has no constant terms, and its solution is indeterminate. This fact reflects the nature of the method of analysis used (see Sections 3.1 and 3.2), since it is assumed that the disturbance is small, without specifying its actual magnitude.

Solving equations (3.20) for $\Delta \delta$, gives

$$\Delta \delta = \frac{D_1(p)}{D(p)},$$

but since $D_1(p) = 0$, the only condition of interest is $D(p) = 0$.

$$D(p) = \begin{vmatrix} J \cdot p^2 + S_{Ed} & -\tau_{do}' \cdot P_{E_d}' \cdot p & -k_V \cdot P_{E_d}' \\[2mm] J \cdot p^2 + S_{E_d'} & P_{E_d}' & 0 \\[2mm] J \cdot p^2 + S_{V_{gd}} & 0 & P_{V_{gd}}' \end{vmatrix} = 0. \quad (3.21)$$

Expansion of the determinant (3.21) yields the characteristic equation:

$$D(p) = J \cdot \tau_d' \cdot p^3 + \left[J + J \cdot k_V \cdot \frac{x_L}{x_{dt}} \right] \cdot p^2 + S_{E_d'} \cdot \tau_d' \cdot p +$$

$$+ \left[S_{E_d} + S_{V_{gd}} \cdot k_V \cdot \frac{x_L}{x_{dt}} \right] = 0, \quad (3.22)$$

where

$$\tau'_d = \tau'_{do} \cdot \frac{x_{dt}}{x'_{dt}} \, .$$

The following new symbols are introduced:

$$a_0 = J \cdot \tau'_d \, ; \quad a_1 = J \, ; \quad a_2 = S_{E'_d} \cdot \tau'_d \, ; \quad a_3 = S_{E_d} \, ;$$

$$\Delta a_1 = J \cdot k_V \cdot \frac{x_L}{x_{dt}} \, ; \quad \Delta a_3 = S_{V_{gd}} \cdot k_V \cdot \frac{x_L}{x_{dt}} \, .$$

Equation (3.22) now becomes:

$$D(p) = a_0 p^3 + (a_1 + \Delta a_1) \, p^2 + a_2 p + (a_3 + \Delta a_3) = 0 \, . \qquad (3.23)$$

The quantities Δa are those parts of the coefficients of the characteristic equation which depend on the action of the regulator.

In the more complicated cases considered later the regulation process also has the same effect of introducing incremental terms Δa which modify some of the coefficients of the characteristic equation.

The best method of control is that which can ensure a wide region of stability, coupled with good regulation of the voltage and large power transfer at large values of load angle in the region of artificial stability.

The Routh–Hurwitz criteria show that the system is stable if all the coefficients of equation (3.23) are positive, i.e.

$$a_0 > 0 \, ; \quad (a_1 + \Delta a_1) > 0 \, ;$$

$$a_2 > 0 \, ; \quad (a_3 + \Delta a_3) > 0 \, ,$$

and if the determinant Δ is also positive,

$$\Delta = [(a_1 + \Delta a_1) \, a_2 - a_0 (a_3 + \Delta a_3)] > 0 \, .$$

When the coefficients are examined in detail, it can be seen that a_2 may be negative when $S_{E'_d} < 0$, and that $(a_3 + \Delta a_3) = S_{E_d} + k_V \cdot \dfrac{x_L}{x_{dt}} \, S_{V_{gd}}$ may also become negative for a certain value of k_V.

The critical value of k_V can be readily found from the condition that the determinant $\Delta > 0$, i.e.

$$\Delta = \left[\left(J + J \cdot k_V \cdot \frac{x_L}{x_{dt}} \right) S_{E'_d} \cdot \tau'_d - J \cdot \tau'_d \left(S_{E_d} + k_V \cdot S_{V_{gd}} \cdot \frac{x_L}{x_{dt}} \right) \right] > 0 \, .$$

This inequality simplifies to:

$$\left[\left(1+k_V \cdot \frac{x_L}{x_{dt}}\right) S_{E_d'} - \left(S_{E_d}+k_V \cdot \frac{x_L}{x_{dt}} \cdot S_{V_{gd}}\right)\right] > 0,$$

from which

$$k_V \leqslant \left(\frac{S_{E_d'} - S_{E_d}}{S_{V_{gd}} - S_{E_d'}}\right) \cdot \frac{x_{dt}}{x_L},$$

so that the maximum permissible value of k_V is

$$(k_V)_{\max} = \frac{x_d - x_d'}{x_d'} \cdot$$

The minimum value of k_V can be found from the condition

$$(a_3 + \Delta a_3) > 0$$

$$(k_V)_{\min} = \frac{S_{E_d}}{S_{V_{gd}}} \cdot \frac{x_{dt}}{x_L} \cdot$$

The two conditions of stability are therefore:

$$S_{E_d'} > 0 \qquad\qquad\qquad (3.24)$$

and

$$(k_V)_{\max} = \frac{x_d - x_d'}{x_d'} \cdot \qquad\qquad (3.24a)$$

The simple voltage-actuated automatic regulator without a dead zone is subject therefore to two operational restrictions:

(1) It is not permissible to operate at such values of angle and of power that $S_{E_d'}$ is close to zero.

(2) It is not permissible to increase the gain beyond $(k_V)_{\max}$, so that the desired condition of constant terminal voltage at all values of load cannot be fully achieved.

It should be emphasized that the over-simplified concept of the excitation system represented mathematically in equation (3.17) by the coefficient of gain k_V, makes equation (3.24a) unsuitable for quantitative calculations. Its practical value lies in the physical insight obtained.

The operating characteristics of the simple regulated system are shown in Fig. 3.18. If the system is unregulated (dotted curves), the power limit corresponding to the limit of stability occurs at $S_{E_d} = 0$.

If it is now assumed that the permissible gain k_V is no longer limited as in equation (3.24a), and that the terminal voltage is maintained constant, the power limit occurs at $S_{V_{gd}} = 0$. The system would, however, become unstable considerably earlier, the oscillation starting at $S_{E'_d} = 0$. This would preclude operation in the region *2-3* along the characteristic $V_g = $ const. Apart from the restriction $S_{E'_d} > 0$, there is also the condition that k_V must not exceed $(k_V)_{max}$ given by equation (3.24a), which makes it impossible to attain the condition $V_g = $ const.

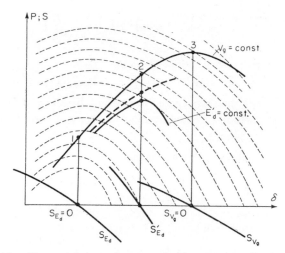

Fig. 3.18. Characteristics of a regulated system and the various stability criteria.

The limit of power corresponding to the actual operational character-istic $P = f(\delta)$, shown by the heavily dotted curve in Fig. 3.18, is there-fore lower than that for $V_g = $ const. The characteristics $P = f(\delta)$ for various values of k_V are displaced from each other as was shown in Fig. 3.17.

In an ordinary electronic regulator designed primarily to maintain the voltage, the gain k_V is usually adjusted to be of the order of 30–40. Under such conditions a part of the characteristic $P = f(\delta)$ applicable for changing values of the induced voltage can to a first approximation be replaced by the characteristic $P_{E'} = f(\delta)$. The limiting values of power and of the load angle are then easily determined.

Exactly similar conclusions are reached when this analysis is applied to the case of a current-actuated regulator for which $\Delta E_{de} = k_I \Delta I$, where ΔI is the change of stator current. Thus, as a very rough approximation, it is permissible to replace an automatically controlled generator, whether voltage or current actuated, by a voltage E' behind an impedance x'_d. The limiting values of the gain factors permitting stable operation are, of course, different for different methods of control.

When the regulator is current-actuated,

$$(k_I)_{max} = \left[\frac{S'_{E_d} - S_{E_d}}{S_{E'_d} - S_{E_d} + (I_\delta / I_{E_d}) \cdot P'_{E_d}} \right] \cdot \frac{x_{dt}}{x_L} ,$$

where

$$I_\delta = \left(\frac{\partial I}{\partial \delta} \right)_{E_d}, \quad \text{and} \quad I_{E_d} = \left(\frac{\partial I}{\partial E_d} \right)_\delta .$$

When the regulator is angle-actuated, $(\Delta E_{de} = k_\delta \Delta \delta)$, the limiting conditions are $S_{E'_d} = 0$ and $k_\delta = (k_\delta)_{max}$, where $(k_\delta)_{max} = S_{E'_d} - S_{E_d}$.

Angle-actuated regulators give somewhat better results in practice than voltage or current-actuated regulators, because they permit the use of larger values of gain.

The minimum values of gain are given by:

for the current-actuated regulator: $(k_I)_{min} = \dfrac{S_{E_d}}{(I_\delta / I_{E_d}) \cdot P'_{E_d} - S_{E_d}} ;$

for the angle-actuated regulator: $(k_\delta)_{min} = - S_{E_d} .$

Operation of the automatic voltage regulator, taking account of the delay in the exciter but neglecting the delay in the regulator

To take account of the delay due to the exciter, equations (3.15) to (3.19) are supplemented by the relation

$$\Delta E_{de} = \frac{\Delta e}{1 + \tau_e \cdot p} , \tag{3.25}$$

where Δe is the change of voltage across the exciter field corresponding to the change of the terminal voltage of the generator,

for the voltage-actuated regulator: $\Delta e = - k_V \cdot \Delta V_{gd} , \tag{3.26}$

for the current-actuated regulator: $\Delta e = k_I \cdot \Delta I , \tag{3.27}$

for the angle-actuated regulator: $\Delta e = k_\delta \cdot \Delta \delta . \tag{3.28}$

By using in equation (3.25) the appropriate value of Δe, and then substituting equation (3.25) into the equation describing the internal conditions in the generator, a system of equations analogous to equation (3.20) is obtained. Solving it in the form $\Delta\delta = \dfrac{D_1(p)}{D(p)}$, the characteristic equation

$D(p) = 0$ is obtained,

$$D(p) = a_0 p^4 + a_1 p^3 + (a_2 + \Delta a_2)\, p^2 + a_3 p + (a_4 + \Delta a_4) = 0 . \qquad (3.29)$$

The main coefficients are given by;

$$a_0 = \tau_e \cdot \tau'_d \cdot J ; \quad a_1 = (\tau'_d + \tau_e) \cdot J ; \quad a_2 = J + \tau'_d \cdot \tau'_e \cdot S'_{E_d};$$
$$a_3 = \tau'_d \cdot S'_{E_d} + \tau_e \cdot S_{E_d} ; \quad a_4 = S_{E_d} .$$

The increments which depend upon the method of actuation are shown in Table 3.1.

TABLE 3.1. VALUES OF Δa

	Voltage-actuated	*Current-actuated*	*Angle-actuated*
Δa_2	$k_V \cdot J \cdot \dfrac{x_L}{x_{dt}}$	$- k_I \cdot J \cdot \dfrac{x_L}{x_{dt}}$	0
Δa_4	$k_V \cdot S_V \cdot \dfrac{x_L}{x_{dt}}$	$k_I \left(\dfrac{I_\delta}{I_{E_d}} \cdot P'_{E_d} - S_{E_d} \right) \cdot \dfrac{x_L}{x_{dt}}$	$k_\delta \cdot \dfrac{x_L}{x_{dt}}$

The Routh–Hurwitz criteria applied to this case yield the following conditions for stability:

$$a_0 > 0 ; \quad a_1 > 0 ; \quad (a_2 + \Delta a_2) > 0 ; \quad a_3 > 0 ; \quad (a_4 + \Delta a_4) > 0 . \qquad (3.30)$$

When examined in detail, the principal inequality to be satisfied is:

$$S'_{E_d} > - \frac{\tau_e}{\tau'_d} \cdot S_{E_d} , \qquad (3.31)$$

and, since S_{E_d} is negative in the region of practical interest, $S'_{E_d} > \xi_1$, where ξ_1 is a positive number.

When this condition is compared with equation (3.24) it can be seen that the presence of inertia in the exciter ($\tau_e \neq 0$) narrows somewhat the region of stable operation. If $\tau_e = 0$, the criterion is $S'_{E_d} > 0$, while in the present case, with $\tau_e \neq 0$, S'_{E_d} must be greater than some positive number ξ_1.

Figure 3.19(a) illustrates the lowering of the power limit (at which oscillations commence) with increase of τ_e in accordance with equation (3.31).

To ensure stability the coefficients of the characteristic equation (3.29) besides satisfying equation (3.30) must also comply with the condition

$$[a_3(a_1 a_2 - a_0 a_3) - a_1^2 a_4] > 0 . \tag{3.32}$$

If the constants of the system and of the regulator are substituted into equation (3.32), the maximum permissible gain factor can be calculated.

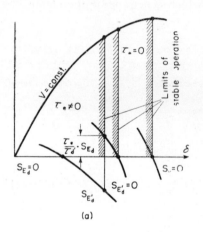

(a)

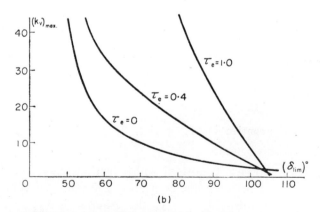

(b)

FIG. 3.19. Regions of stable operation with (a) $\tau_e = 0$ and $\tau_e \neq 0$, and (b) magnitudes of the maximum permissible gain factor for different values of exciter time constant.

The value of the gain factor depends on the method of control:
Voltage-actuated regulator:

$$(k_V)_{max} = \frac{\left(\dfrac{S_{E_d'} - S_{E_d}}{S_V - S_{E_d'}}\right) \cdot \dfrac{x_{dt}}{x_L}\left[1 + \dfrac{\tau_e^2}{J}\left(\dfrac{\tau_d' \cdot S_{E_d'} + \tau_e \cdot S_{E_d}}{\tau_e + \tau_d'}\right)\right]}{1 + \dfrac{\tau_e}{\tau_d'} \cdot \left(\dfrac{S_V - S_{E_d}}{S_V - S_{E_d'}}\right)}.$$

Current-actuated regulator:

$$(k_I)_{max} = \frac{(S_{E_d'} - S_{E_d}) \cdot \left[1 + \dfrac{\tau_e^2}{J}\left(\dfrac{\tau_d' \cdot S_{E_d'} - \tau_e \cdot S_{E_d}}{\tau_e + \tau_d'}\right)\right]}{S_{E_d'} - S_{E_d} + \dfrac{I_\delta}{I_{E_d}} \cdot P_{E_d}'\left(1 + \dfrac{\tau_e}{\tau_d'}\right)}.$$ (3.33)

Angle-actuated regulator:

$$(k_\delta)_{max} = \left(\frac{S_{E_d'} - S_{E_d}}{\tau_e + \tau_d'}\right) \cdot \frac{x_{dt}}{x_L} \cdot \tau_d'\left[1 + \frac{\tau_e^2}{J}\left(\frac{\tau_d' \cdot S_{E_d'} + \tau_e \cdot S_{E_d}}{\tau_e + \tau_d'}\right)\right].$$

Equations (3.33) show that an increase in τ_e leads to a larger critical value of gain and, hence, to a more constant voltage. It should be emphasized that the critical value of gain is a function of S_{E_d}, $S_{E_d'}$, and S_V, and hence depends on the load conditions. For a particular case the critical value of gain can be determined as a function of δ for different values of τ_e (Fig. 3.19(b)).

The curves of Fig. 3.19(b) are drawn for a particular case, but similar curves apply for any other system. Whatever the system, two conditions, equations (3.31) and (3.33), must be satisfied simultaneously, leading to the requirement that $k \leqslant k_{max}$.

In attempting to comply with this requirement it must be borne in mind that operation at large values of the load angle makes it necessary to use a smaller value of k_{max} leading to a less satisfactory voltage curve (Fig. 3.19). These curves also show that if the maximum value of δ is 90–100°, it is desirable to increase τ_e, thus leading to a larger value of k_{max} and a flatter voltage curve.

In ordinary electronic excitation regulators, primarily designed to maintain the voltage, the exciter time constant may be artificially increased by employing an auxiliary feed-back loop actuated by the exciter voltage. The equivalent value of the time constant τ_e may then reach 10–20 sec. Although this precludes operation at large values of δ, the action of the regulator is stabilized in the best manner, and the voltage can be maintained constant to within 2 or 3 per cent over wide changes of the generator load ((3.31) and (3.33)).

The discussion given above brings out clearly the contradictory nature of the requirements of stable operation and of good voltage control.

The difficulties in selecting the appropriate coefficient of gain in regulators which are current or angle actuated are greater still. The lowering of gain, to ensure stability when operating at large angles, adversely affects the voltage regulation, leading to a steep fall in voltage when the load is heavy and a steep rise when it is light.

One way out of the difficulty is to use non-linear elements, which automatically adjust the gain as a function of load. Alternatively, secondary voltage regulators or compensating devices may be used, acting more slowly than the main regulator, and re-establishing the terminal voltage of the generator with a certain delay. Smaller values of gain are adequate with this arrangement, since the secondary regulator is capable of bringing the generator voltage back to its value V_{g0}. The action of the secondary regulator is illustrated in Fig. 3.20.

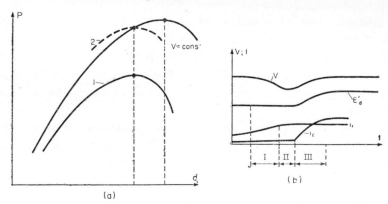

FIG. 3.20. Action of the secondary regulator: (*a*) the characteristic $P = f(\delta)$; (1) $E_d' = $ const; (2) induced voltage increased due to action of secondary regulator; (*b*) the voltages V, E_d', and the main and secondary regulator currents i_r and i_c as functions of time; I — time interval during which the main regulator is effective; II — time delay of secondary regulator; III — time interval during which the secondary regulator is effective.

A much better method of improving the action of a regulator, so as to make it possible to operate at $V_g = $ const without danger of self-oscillation, is to utilize for purposes of control not only the changes ΔI, ΔV, and $\Delta \delta$, but also their first and second time-rates of change. This method of control is called *forced regulation*.

3.5.   Steady-state Stability of Simple Systems with Forced Regulation

The term "forced regulation" is not a very precise one. It implies that the method of control is particularly effective in modifying the operational performance of the machine, and in producing a constant, or even a rising, voltage at the terminals of the machine or at the sending end of a transmission line. This performance is achieved mainly by making the regulator respond to the derivatives pI, p^2I, $p\delta$, $p^2\delta$, pV, and p^2V.

With forced regulation stability is maintained right up to the power limit, so that the maximum power transmitted becomes equal to the power limit of the transmission line. It is hardly necessary to point out that forced control is of special importance in power systems where the maximum power is limited by the criteria of steady-state stability.

The effectiveness of regulators, sensitive not only to the variables themselves, but also to their derivatives, can be broadly ascribed to their ability to "predict" the future course of events. Thus, for example, a regulator sensitive to the change of angle δ, cannot act until the change $\Delta\delta$ has become sufficiently great. On the other hand, a change in the operational conditions has an immediate effect on the acceleration $p^2\delta$. In consequence, the use of $p^2\delta$ as a control signal makes it possible to "predict" the future change, and to control the operation in the desired direction from the very instant at which the change is initiated.

The use of $p\delta$ as a control signal is analogous to the increase of damping and is often of assistance in causing a rapid decay of oscillations. Broadly similar effects arise from the use of pV, p^2V, pI, and p^2I as control signals.

In general, the most effective regulators are those which employ combined methods of control, responding both to the variables themselves and to their derivatives.

Method of deriving the differential equations for a power system supplied by generators with forced excitation regulators

Figure 3.21 represents a power system in which the generators are equipped with forced excitation regulators.

The quantities to be controlled are the terminal voltage of the generator V_g, the stator current I, and the displacement angle δ of the rotor relative to the bus-bar voltage V of a large system.

The block diagram of the regulator sensitive to the first and the second derivatives (Fig. 3.21) can be simplified by assuming that the double differentiator DD generating the second derivative may be represented by a single-element with a time constant τ_{r_2} rather than by two elements connected in cascade, as found in a real regulator.

The time constant of the rectifier and filter element Rec is denoted by τ_r.

The differential equation of the rectifier for different methods of control is:

$$\left.\begin{aligned}
\Delta\delta &= \tau_r \cdot pe_1 + e_1 \\
\Delta V_g &= \tau_r \cdot pe_1 + e_1 \\
\Delta I &= \tau_r \cdot pe_1 + e_1
\end{aligned}\right\}, \qquad (3.34)$$

where e_1 is the voltage supplied to the measuring and differentiating elements M and D.

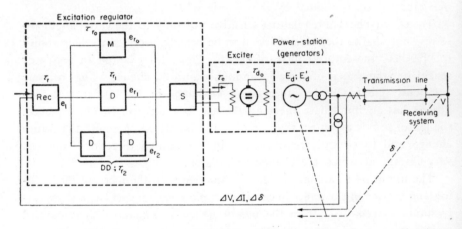

FIG. 3.21. Power system with forced excitation regulator. Rec—rectifying element with time-constant τ_r; M—measuring element with time-constant τ_{r_0}; D—differentiating element with time-constant τ_{r_1}; DD—double differentiating element; S—summator element.

The delay of the measuring element M can in practice be made so small that it may be neglected ($\tau_{r_0} = 0$).

The delay of the differentiating members D and DD, however, may be significant. Their time constants are denoted by τ_{r_1} and τ_{r_2} respectively.

The differential equations of the elements M, D, and DD are as follows:
Measuring element M:

$$e_{r_0} = k_0 e_1. \qquad (3.35)$$

Differentiating element D:

$$\tau_{r_1} \cdot pe_{r_1} + e_{r_1} = k_1 \cdot pe_1. \qquad (3.36)$$

Double differentiating element DD:

$$\tau_{r_2} \cdot p e_{r_2} + e_{r_2} = k_2 \cdot p^2 e_1 . \tag{3.37}$$

The gain coefficients k_1 and k_2 are calculated so as to include the combined gain of the whole regulator system.

The summator element S delivers a voltage e to the field winding of the exciter

$$e = e_{r_0} + e_{r_1} + e_{r_2} .$$

The equations of the generator system controlled by forced excitation regulators may, as a first approximation, be written as follows:

$$(J \cdot p^2 + P_d \cdot p) \Delta \delta = -\Delta P \tag{3.38}$$

$$\tau_{d0} \cdot p \Delta E'_d + \Delta E_d = \Delta E_{de} \tag{3.39}$$

$$\Delta E_{de} = \frac{\Delta e}{\tau_e \cdot p + 1} \tag{3.40}$$

where Δe depends upon the method of control

$$(\Delta e_\delta , \quad \Delta e_I , \quad \text{or} \quad \Delta e_V) .$$

Combining equations (3.34) to (3.37),

$$\left.\begin{aligned}
\Delta e_\delta &= \left(k_{\delta_0} + \frac{k_{\delta_1} \cdot p}{\tau_{r_1} p + 1} + \frac{k_{\delta_2} \cdot p^2}{\tau_{r_2} p + 1} \right) \cdot \left(\frac{\Delta \delta}{\tau_r p + 1} \right) \\
\Delta e_I &= \left(k_{I_0} + \frac{k_{I_1} \cdot p}{\tau_{r_1} p + 1} + \frac{k_{I_2} \cdot p^2}{\tau_{r_2} p + 1} \right) \cdot \left(\frac{\Delta I}{\tau_r p + 1} \right) \\
\Delta e_V &= \left(k_{V_0} + \frac{k_{V_1} \cdot p}{\tau_{r_1} p + 1} + \frac{k_{V_2} \cdot p^2}{\tau_{r_2} p + 1} \right) \cdot \left(\frac{\Delta V_g}{\tau_r p + 1} \right)
\end{aligned}\right\} . \tag{3.41}$$

These expressions can be simplified if it is assumed that the time constant τ_r of the rectifier element Rec is negligibly small ($\tau_r = 0$).

$$\left.\begin{aligned}
\Delta e'_\delta &= \left(k_{\delta_0} + \frac{k_{\delta_1} \cdot p}{\tau_{r_1} p + 1} + \frac{k_{\delta_2} \cdot p^2}{\tau_{r_2} p + 1} \right) \Delta \delta \\
\Delta e'_I &= \left(k_{I_0} + \frac{k_{I1} \cdot p}{\tau_{r_1} p + 1} + \frac{k_{I2} \cdot p^2}{\tau_{r_2} p + 1} \right) \Delta I \\
\Delta e'_V &= \left(k_{V_0} + \frac{k_{V_1} \cdot p}{\tau_{r_1} p + 1} + \frac{k_{V_2} \cdot p^2}{\tau_{r_2} p + 1} \right) \Delta V_g
\end{aligned}\right\} . \tag{3.41a}$$

For the general case of a regulator of any type one may write

$$\Delta e = \frac{W_u(p) \cdot \Delta_u V}{1 + \tau_p \cdot p} , \tag{3.41b}$$

where $W_u(p)$ is the transfer function of the regulator,

$$W_u(p) = k_{u_0} + \frac{k_{u_1} \cdot p}{\tau_{r_1} \cdot p + 1} + \frac{k_{u_2} \cdot p^2}{\tau_{r_2} \cdot p + 1} . \tag{3.41c}$$

To obtain the two additional equations required, the method of the previous section is used (see equation (3.19)) by writing for the increments of power,

and

$$\left.\begin{aligned} \Delta P &= P'_{E_d} \cdot \Delta E_d + S_{E_d} \cdot \Delta\delta \\[2mm] \Delta P &= P'_{E'_d} \cdot \Delta E'_d + S'_{E_d} \cdot \Delta\delta \end{aligned}\right\} . \tag{3.42}$$

The solution of this system of equations is completely analogous to that discussed above for the simple system, although it is much more laborious in detail, the resulting characteristic equation being of a higher order than before.

3.6.   General Assessment of the Stability of Systems with Controlled Excitation

The introduction of automatic excitation control has considerably widened the region within which stable operation is possible. The general conclusions reached are summarized in this section by considering the behaviour of the system shown in Fig. 3.22(a) when the power delivered by it increases. The problem is to determine the power limit associated with the various kinds of regulator and the nature of the process when stability is lost.

With no control ($E_d = E_{d0}$), the maximum power is given by point *1* in Fig. 3.22 (*b*). In the lower part of the figure, showing δ as a function of time, the point A at which $S_{E_d} = 0$, indicates the instant at which the machine falls out of synchronism. The loss of synchronism in this case is aperiodic.

If a regulator with a dead zone is used, the power limit is raised. For a constant value of V_g the limit is given by point *2*. The stability region, measured in terms of the angle, is, however, not widened. The machine loses synchronism at the same point A, although the process may now be either aperiodic or oscillatory.

The region of stability (both in terms of power and of angle) is widened when continuously-acting regulators are used. With a gain of the order of 100–200 they can maintain an almost constant voltage at the terminals of the generator or at the input terminals of a line, but self-oscillation starts at some angle δ_1 larger than that at which $S_{E_d} = 0$ but smaller than that at which $S_{E'_d} = 0$. The onset of this process is indicated in the lower part of Fig. 3.22(b) by the point B. The corresponding

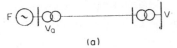

(a)

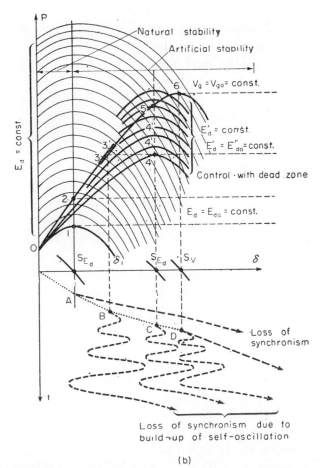

(b)

FIG. 3.22. Power limits attainable with various methods of excitation control and loss of synchronism caused by failure to maintain stability.

range of maximum power attainable along the characteristic $P = f(\delta)$ for $V_g = $ const is indicated by the thickened segment *3–3'*. The maximum power for a long line may be somewhat less than that corresponding to the condition $E'_d = E'_{do}$ (point *4*), or somewhat larger for the case of a short line.

If the gain is reduced, operation at angles greater than δ_1 becomes possible. With gain of the order 4–8 the operation is stable up to the angle at which $S_{E'_d} = 0$ (point *C* in the lower part of Fig. 3.22(*b*)). In this case $E'_d =$ const, and V_g falls with increase of load. The maximum power is given by the point *4* on the characteristic $E'_d = E'_{do}$ $=$ const.

With forced-excitation regulators the machines can operate at still larger values of angle while maintaining constant terminal voltage. The point of operation moves along the segment *3–6* of the characteristic $V_g =$ const. The loss of stability occurs in this case approximately at the point *D*, where $S_V \simeq 0$; the process of losing synchronism may be either oscillatory (with growing amplitude) or aperiodic.

In assessing the possible advantages afforded by automatic voltage regulation the use of secondary astatic compensating devices for correcting the voltage must be considered. Their action can be illustrated by the characteristics shown in Fig. 3.22. If it is assumed that the gain has a small value of the order of 4–8, the increase of load (and of the angle δ) is accompanied by a falling terminal voltage V_g. This fall of voltage is compensated by devices subsidiary to the main regulator and operating much more slowly.

The process of voltage control in this case is somewhat similar (although the analogy is not complete) to that provided by a regulator with a dead zone. The correction is made by increasing the voltages E_d or E'_d, and the operating characteristics are 0–4', 0–4'', etc., instead of 0–4. The maximum power with an ordinary regulator (without derivative control) is indicated by the point *5*, where $S_{E'_d} = 0$.

Mathematically the difference between the action of a regulator of the ordinary type and a forced-excitation regulator is indicated by the presence of the incremental terms in the coefficients of the characteristic equation of the system. These incremental terms arise because the forced-excitation regulator is sensitive to the time rates of change of the variables. The determination of the conditions of stability for the forced-excitation regulator by the method of small oscillations remains unaltered, however. It consists of establishing a set of linearized equations holding for the regulator and the excitation system.

The equations obtained form a set of homogeneous equations without constant terms. In the most general form they may be written as:

$$A_1 x + A_2 y + A_3 z + \ldots + A_n \gamma = 0 \ \Big\}$$

$$B_1 x + B_2 y + B_3 z + \ldots + B_n \gamma = 0 \ \Big\} \ \text{etc.,} \qquad (3.43)$$

where the coefficients A, B, etc., contain the system constants and various powers of the differential operator p. The quantities x, y, z, $.. \gamma$ represent the variables.

Such a set of equations is indeterminate. Solution for the different variables leads to expressions of the form:

$$x = \frac{D_1(p)}{D(p)} \ ; \qquad y = \frac{D_2(p)}{D(p)} \ , \ \text{etc.,}$$

in which $D_1(p) = 0$, $D_2(p) = 0$, etc.,

A non-trivial solution (though still indeterminate) is obtained only when the characteristic equation $D(p) = 0$ is satisfied.

The mathematical part of the investigation of stability, and of the determination of the best method of voltage control is thus reduced in the main to the determination of the roots p of the characteristic equation. These roots are functions of the coefficients of the characteristic equation which has the general form:

$$D(p) = (a_0 + \Delta a_0) \cdot p^n + (a_1 + \Delta a_1) \cdot p^{n-1} + \ldots + (a_n + \Delta a_n) = 0 \ ,$$

where the terms a_k are unaffected by the regulator, while the terms Δa_k depend on its action.

The problem of investigating the steady-state stability of *a given system employing a given method of control* reduces to the analysis of the character of the roots for given values of the coefficients $(a_k + \Delta a_k)$.

The problem of determining the best method of control for *a given system* is reduced to the finding of values for the incremental terms Δa_k, such that all the coefficients $(a_k + \Delta a_k)$ remain positive under all conditions of operation. Furthermore, since the characteristic equation is of a high order, there are also other conditions to be satisfied to ensure that the real parts of the roots remain positive and the operation of the system stable.

The choice of suitable gain factors also requires special consideration. Thus, in the case of a regulator of the ordinary type, it is important to remember that simplicity and reliability in the design call for constant values of gain. The value of gain chosen should be the highest permitted by the most unfavourable operating conditions.

Sometimes other considerations may restrict the freedom of choice of a suitable value of gain. Thus, for a voltage actuated regulator the value of $(k_{V_0})_{max}$ is limited by the conditions of stability, and these may prove to be decisive in making the final choice.

In a forced-excitation regulator, which is voltage-actuated, an increase in the value of the gain factor k_{V_0} necessitates a very considerable increase in the factors k_{V_1} and k_{V_2}. The values of these factors in most cases are restricted, however, by the possibility of high frequency oscillations (which lie outside the scope of this book). Thus the value of $(k_{V_0})_{max}$ is also restricted.

In forced-excitation regulators which are angle-actuated, the gain factor k_{δ_0} can be chosen freely. It can be made very large, since its value has hardly any effect on the factors k_{δ_1} and k_{δ_2}. However if k_{δ_0} is large, any shock to the system produces a sudden change of voltage. A secondary compensating regulator may act too slowly to smooth out the effect of the shock, and it may be preferable for operation at normal loads to reduce the value of k_{δ_0}.

The introduction of non-linearity to change the magnitude of k_{δ_0} as the load varies does not eliminate the need for the secondary regulator to maintain the output voltage under all load conditions.

If the regulator is actuated by the stator current and its derivatives, the gain factor k_{I_0} considerably restricts the range of values of k_{I_1} and k_{I_2} for which the operation remains stable. This may lead to difficulties in adjusting the regulator and make it necessary to use variable gain factors.

Here, too, even if the gain factor k_{I_0} is made to vary non-linearly a secondary regulator may still be required.

3.7. The Behaviour of an Electrical System when Subjected to Small Sustained Disturbances

In the discussion of steady-state stability given in this chapter the motion of the system was considered to be free, the initial disturbance being due to a force acting for a very short time. In accordance with this assumption the resulting equations contained no terms representing driving forces.

Now it will be assumed that the system is subjected to sustained disturbing forces.

For the simple case of a single station feeding an infinite bus through a transmission line the equation of motion is:

$$J \cdot p^2 \Delta\delta + \Delta P + \Delta P_0 = 0 , \tag{3.44}$$

where

ΔP is the change of power due to a change of the angle $\Delta\delta$, and ΔP_0

is the change of power produced by various causes, such as change of load, change of output of the prime mover, etc.

Here, as before,

$$\Delta P = \frac{\partial P}{\partial \delta} \cdot \Delta \delta = S_{E_d} \cdot \Delta \delta \,.$$

When substituted in equation (3.44), the latter becomes

$$(J \cdot p^2 + S_{E_d}) \cdot \Delta \delta = -\Delta P_0 \,,$$

i.e. an equation containing a driving force. When solved for $\Delta \delta$, this becomes

$$\Delta \delta = - \frac{\Delta P_0}{J \cdot p^2 + S_{E_d}} \,. \tag{3.45}$$

Equation (3.45) is an operational equation, in which $\Delta \delta$ is a function of the operator p. Applying the rules of operational calculus, $\Delta \delta$ can be expressed as a function of time

$$\Delta \delta(t) = -\Delta P_0 (\varepsilon^{p_1 t} + \varepsilon^{p_2 t}) \,,$$

where

$$p_{1,2} = \pm \sqrt{\left(- \frac{S_{E_d}}{J} \right)} \,.$$

If the original assumption of small amplitude of all disturbances remains valid, the conditions for stability of the system are unaffected by the presence of the sustained disturbance ΔP_0. Thus, equation (3.44) can be re-written

$$\Delta \delta = \frac{D_1(p)}{D(p)} \,,$$

where

$$D_1(p) = \Delta P_0 \,, \quad \text{and} \quad D(p) = J \cdot p^2 + S_{E_d} \,.$$

The nature of the motion is determined by the roots of $D(p)=0$, while $D_1(p)$ affects the quantitative side of the process, determining the amplitude of oscillations if the system is stable, or the rate of increase of the amplitude (i.e. the time constant) if the system is unstable.

In more complicated cases when one or more sustained disturbances are present, driving force terms appear in one or more equations describing the motion. The equations analogous to (3.43) are now of the form:

$$\left. \begin{array}{l} A_1 x + A_2 y + A_3 z + \ldots + A_n \gamma = \Delta \xi_1 \\[4pt] B_1 x + B_2 y + B_3 z + \ldots + B_n \gamma = 0 \\[4pt] C_1 x + C_2 y + C_3 z + \ldots + C_n \gamma = \Delta \xi_2 \end{array} \right\} \quad \text{etc.}$$

It is obvious that $D_1(p)$, $D_2(p)$, etc., are not equal to zero, and that the variables x, y, z, ... are fully determined.

In some cases it is desirable to obtain an assessment of the magnitudes of the quantities involved in a process. In such an assessment the changes in voltage, frequency, current, angle, etc., would be expressed as functions of other variables or of the system parameters.

The conditions for stability determined by the analysis of the characteristic equations $D(p) = 0$ are obviously unaffected by the magnitudes of the quantities $\Delta\xi_k$.

The method of small oscillations, discussed in Sections 3.2 to 3.6 merely as a means of determining conditions of stability, has, however, a wider application. The method can yield, not only the necessary and sufficient conditions for stability, but can also, as shown in the present section, be used to find the various variables as functions of time.

The student confronted for the first time with stability problems in power systems often looks for a connecting link between the methods employed in studying large and small disturbances. In the former case the differential equations are solved by applying the well-developed step-by-step methods, using a network analyser. Is it not more rational, asks the student, to study the transient stability of a system under the influence of disturbing forces of small amplitude, rather than its steady-state stability? The desirability of making a full analysis for a definite disturbance of a given system, rather than a general analysis in terms of stability criteria, is a question often raised in other fields. The idea is attractive if the disturbances on which the calculations are to be based can be arrived at by statistical methods.

In the case of electrical power systems, however, methods of selecting the appropriate nature and magnitude of the disturbance have not yet been worked out. Besides, in a complicated regulated system the loss of stability can occur after several cycles of small oscillations, the amplitude of which may at first decrease, and then begin to grow again. On the other hand, a system which is stable may be subject to oscillations which build up at first but are damped out eventually.

Consequently if a solution by the step-by-step method is attempted, a large number of intervals must be used, leading to large cumulative errors, particularly since the changes of voltages and currents are small. This may make the results obtained from the analyser too inaccurate. It appears therefore that this approach can hardly be expected to yield results comparable with those obtained by Lyapunov's method, which is particularly powerful in revealing the essential properties of any regulated system, and of the manner in which the system is affected by the particular means of regulation. It is likely that the more detailed studies of stability of power systems will in the future supplement rather than replace analysis by the method of small oscillations.

The critical regions in which a system is likely to become unstable are of particular interest. By applying Lyapunov's method it is possible to separate out a certain danger zone where a sudden finite disturbance may cause instability, even though the real parts of all the roots of the characteristic equation remain negative. In such regions it is advisable to investigate not only the linearized equations written as a first approximation but also the equations in which the non-linearities are retained and which represent more exactly the real behaviour of the system.

CHAPTER 4

RECOMMENDATIONS FOR PRACTICAL STABILITY CALCULATIONS

4.1. Calculations of Steady-state Stability

The ability of a system to return to its initial state following a small disturbance has been defined as its *steady-state stability*.

This definition leads naturally to the method of small oscillations discussed in the previous chapter as the most exact means of calculation. In certain cases and for rough estimates, simplified methods are often adequate, yielding the so-called "practical stability criteria".

(a) Method of small oscillations

This method is applicable to systems of any configuration and makes it possible to take all the factors into account. In this sense, it is universal. It can be criticized, however, from the practical point of view, since it is very laborious in detail.

The application of the method of small oscillations is essential in the following cases:

(1) For a system employing devices of untested design which may give rise to self-oscillation under normal operating conditions.

(2) In cases where self-oscillation may occur under certain special operating conditions.

(3) For checking the design of a system requiring precise analysis of its conditions of operation, for refining test results, for determining factors of safety, etc.

The mathematical labour involved in applying the method of small oscillations is reasonably light for a single station connected to an infinite bus, or for two stations feeding a common load.

The method of small oscillations makes it possible to determine whether a given system is, or is not, stable under given operating conditions, but it does not provide a means of assessing the available margin of stability. To determine this margin two methods may be used. The first is based on the requirement that the numerical value of the real part a_n of any root of the characteristic equation should not be less than some number λ. The margin of safety k, expressed as a percentage, may then be defined as

$$k = \frac{a_n}{\lambda} \cdot 100 \,.$$

The margin of stability may also be assessed by applying the method of separation of domains (Section 3.3). When forced excitation regulators are used it is possible to determine the margin of safety by plotting the

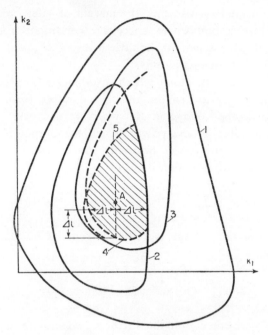

FIG. 4.1. The determination of the minimum value of the margin of safety from the position of the operating point A within the region of stability of the function $k_2 = f(k_1)$. Curve: 1, for $\delta_{12} = 30°$; 2, for $\delta_{12} = 90°$; 3, for $\delta_{12} = 120°$; 4, for conditions of falling load voltage; 5, for operation with parts of the transmission line disconnected. The shaded area is the region of stability common to all conditions of operation. Δl is the distance of the operating point A from the stability boundary.

relation $k_1 = f(k_2)$ connecting two gain factors (Fig. 4.1), and by checking whether there is an overlap between the operational zones when:
(1) the power output is increased,
(2) the line configuration is altered,
(3) the working voltage is reduced.

The margin of safety is considered adequate if the operating point A lies within the common zone and is not anywhere nearer to its boundary than a certain distance Δl which, when expressed as a percentage of k_1 and k_2, is not less than k.

There exists as yet no accepted standard for the margin of safety determined in this way. It is reasonably safe to assume that if the value of k exceeds 5 per cent any possible inaccuracies in calculation are adequately covered.

The second method of assessing the margin of safety requires a series of calculations for a number of successive conditions approaching the stability limit of the system, its behaviour being checked at each stage by the method of small oscillations.

The choice of the path along which instability is approached is arbitrary. It is usual either to increase the power output from a distant station, or to reduce the voltage in the receiving network.

If the critical value of the power (when the output is gradually increased) is P_{max} and the power normally transmitted P_0, the margin of safety k_P expressed in per cent is

$$k_P = \frac{P_{max} - P_0}{P_0} \cdot 100 \ .$$

Similarly, when the voltage is reduced from its normal value V_0 to its critical value V_{cr}

$$k_V = \frac{V_0 - V_{cr}}{V_0} \cdot 100 \ .$$

It is normally accepted that the factor k_P should lie in the region of 10–15 per cent, and the factor k_V in the region of 10–12 per cent under conditions of continuous operation. For a short period following a fault a figure of 5–10 per cent for k_P and 5–7 per cent for k_V may be considered adequate.

(b) Practical stability criteria

These are derived from simplified methods of calculation which take no account of possible self-oscillation, and cannot therefore be said to give a complete picture of the behaviour of the system.

Different methods of calculation lead to different kinds of criteria. The usefulness of any given result depends on the configuration of the system, and it is important to select for the preliminary analysis a method providing the most suitable criterion.

Thus a system containing one station far removed from the centre of the load, and a group of stations near it, can be reduced to a system of two stations feeding a common load.

The stability criteria for this case are:

$$\frac{dP}{d\delta} > 0, \quad \text{or} \quad \frac{dV}{dP} < 0.$$

The determination of $dP/d\delta$ is simplest if the load voltage can be assumed to remain constant, but becomes more complicated if the voltage V_L at the load terminals varies due to the redistribution of load between the distant and the local stations. The load impedance Z_L can, for this purpose, be treated as a constant.

As a further refinement the non-linearity of the load can be taken into consideration, by making use of the static characteristics $P_L = f(V)$ and $Q_L = \varphi(V)$, and determining the corresponding changes of voltage.

In addition, the change of voltage with change of frequency is sometimes taken into account, using the characteristics $P_L = \varphi(f)$ and $Q = \varphi(f)$.

Generally, it is sufficient to compute the voltage regulation only, allowing for the drop in frequency following a fault, and assuming it to remain constant thereafter.

The calculations indicated above may be modified in various ways:

(1) Saturation in the generators may or may not be considered.

(2) An assumption may be made that a certain voltage (e.g. E_d' or E') remains constant while the load redistribution takes place, and the regulation of the generators computed accordingly. The voltage may be assumed to remain constant until $S_{E_d'} = 0$ if a secondary voltage regulator is used.

(3) Instead of assuming a redistribution of power between stations for an unspecified load, the reactive component of the load may be assumed to alter by a certain amount, and the critical power determined by considering $\dfrac{dP}{d\delta}$ under conditions of falling voltage across the load.

The margin of safety for cases (1) and (2) is determined as

$$k_P = \frac{P_{\max} - P_0}{P_0} \cdot 100,$$

and for case (3) as

$$k_V = \frac{V_0 - V_{cr}}{V_0} \cdot 100.$$

The accepted figures for the factors k_P and k_V are the same as before.

For a system containing three or more stations, $\dfrac{dP}{d\delta}$ is calculated by considering the redistribution of power in the system when either:

(1) the load angles of all stations except one remain constant, or

(2) the power output from all but two stations remains constant.

These calculations are reduced to the computation of the synchronizing components of power. It may again be assumed that a certain voltage (depending on the nature of the voltage control used in a station) remains constant, either treating the load impedance Z_L as constant, or using the static characteristics as described above.

For concentrated systems with power distribution points located near the stations supplying a number of composite loads, it is recommended that the stability of the stations should be checked by using the criterion

$$\frac{d(\Delta Q_g)}{dV} < 0 .$$

The margin of safety in this case is

$$k_V = \frac{V_0 - V_{cr}}{V_0} \cdot 100 ,$$

where V_{cr} is the value of voltage corresponding to the condition

$$\frac{d(\Delta Q_g)}{dV} = 0 .$$

The recommended magnitude of k_V remains the same as before.

For systems in which stations remote from the load have approximately the same phase displacements of voltage $(\delta_{L1}, \delta_{L2})$ the most dangerous condition is brought about by instability of the load. The phase angles associated with each generator are little affected thereby, remaining either unchanged or changing by the same amount $(\delta_{12} = \text{const})$.

Such a system may be replaced by a single equivalent station, and its stability tested by applying the criterion

$$\frac{dE}{dV} > 0 .$$

The critical voltage V_{cr} is determined by a semi-graphical method described in Section 1.4. The margin of safety

$$k_V = \frac{V_0 - V_{cr}}{V_0} \cdot 100$$

should not be less than 15 per cent in normal operation and not less than 10 per cent following a fault.

The criterion dP/df is rarely used in practice and need not be considered in detail.

The methods of determining steady-state stability just discussed are applicable both for the design and for the operation of power systems. The most important and frequent problems in which they are employed are:

(1) Determination of the maximum power that can be transmitted with given values of voltage at the station and at the receiving end of the transmission line.

(2) Determination of critical values of voltage for a given flow of power in a given system.

(3) Check of the operational performance of a system by the use of stability criteria.

(4) Determination of the power-handling capacity of the main interconnexions of a power system.

(5) Effect of extensions on the stability of a system.

(6) Choice of the most suitable method of control and the best excitation system for the alternators and synchronous condensers, to obtain improved steady-state stability of separate stations or of the system as a whole, or to increase the power-handling capacity of long transmission lines.

(7) Determination of the requirements to be satisfied by the connexion scheme adopted, or of the necessary changes to attain or to improve the steady-state stability.

(8) Investigation of the stability of a remote load supplied by a system to ascertain the available margin of safety.

All these calculations should be carried out for the conditions of normal operation as well as for those pertaining to a period immediately following a fault.

4.2. Calculations of Transient Stability

Transient stability calculations are made to determine the process of transition from one condition of operation to another, after the system has been subjected to a shock. If the system survives the shock without loss of synchronism by any of the major stations, its stability is considered to be adequate.

Stability calculations are usually carried out for various types of short circuit, occurring at the most vulnerable points of the system when it is carrying the maximum permissible load.

For a system consisting of a single station feeding a constant bus through a long transmission line, the most vulnerable point is near the generator terminals.

A stability calculation must take into account all measures introduced to improve stability, such as the earthing of transformer neutrals through a resistor or a choke, or the use of excitation regulators. Such special measures as mechanical braking should not be considered, because their frequent application is undesirable, and their control under single and two-phase short-circuit conditions is difficult.

A single-phase fault is normally assumed for transient stability calculations. A two-phase fault to earth need only be considered if the single-phase calculation shows the receiving network to be deficient in power by an amount in excess of 5 per cent (when the available reserves are included). If, in a given system, the power is deficient by less than 5 per cent, or if the system equipment and the conditions in the consumers' installations can allow asynchronous operation, calculations for a single-phase fault are considered adequate.

The calculations should be carried out either for the normal continuous operating conditions of the system, or for the maximum load condition, if the system is designed to deliver its maximum power for long periods. Abnormal conditions arising during overhaul of the equipment need not be considered, since at such times the load carried by the system can always be reduced to satisfy the conditions of steady-state and transient stability. The calculations must determine the available power margin, as well as the steady-state and transient stability of the system. Although it is usual to consider only a single-phase fault, the designer must make certain that stability is likely to be maintained even if a more serious fault (two-phases to earth or three-phases) should occur. For these conditions special measures may be required in order to increase the stability of the system.

The economic side of the question also demands consideration, the cost of any additional equipment being balanced against the probability of loss arising from any given type of fault. The stability calculation must also allow for the possibility of using automatic reclosing in each phase, or of operating with a phase disconnected.

When considering two- or three-phase faults, the stability may be allowed to depend entirely on the use of forced excitation, the voltage being increased automatically during the period immediately following a fault.

If these measures are insufficient, the advisibility of allowing prolonged asynchronous operation with subsequent resynchronization should be considered, taking account of the effect of the reactive power component on the operation of the system as a whole. If, as a result of the analysis, it becomes evident that asynchronous operation followed by automatic resynchronization is undesirable, the provision of mechanical or electrical braking devices should be considered, since they can help to maintain synchronism or to improve the conditions for resynchronization, if synchronism is lost.

To determine the efficacy of the braking devices, it is necessary to assess the probability of occurrence of a given type of fault at the most vulnerable point (from the point view of stability) of the transmission line. It must also be considered whether the severity of the fault may be reduced by a shift of the point at which it occurs, or as a result of arcing.

If the use of braking devices, which are the most powerful means of improving the transient stability, is not warranted, various kinds of auxiliary equipment may be considered for improving the load-carrying capacity of the line. Particularly careful consideration must then be given to the probability of occurrence of the various types of short-circuit fault and the extent of the consequent damage.

Stability calculations for weak transmission links must take into account the variation of the load both in the transmission line and in the receiving system. Control of the prime movers at the transmitting end is an important means to this end. If should also be ascertained that stability is maintained if any one of the synchronous condensers operates asynchronously, or if equalizing surges of power flow in order to maintain constant frequency in the system. The stability of a small capacity line, connected in parallel with a main line, may be lost when the main line is disconnected. When calculating the transient stability of a fully loaded system, the time required to clear a short-circuit should be taken as $0 \cdot 10$–$0 \cdot 12$ sec for lines of 400–600 kV, and as $0 \cdot 18$–$0 \cdot 20$ sec for lines of 110–220 kV.

The designer has a choice of three methods of calculating transient stability:

(a) Approximate calculations

Such calculations are carried out to make a rough check of operational conditions. They can be used to choose which of several alternatives should be investigated further, or for a rough check of the various means of improving stability for a given condition of operation.

In calculations of this kind it is usual to assume that E' or E'_d remains constant. The equal-area criterion is used to determine the stability, the margin of safety being estimated from the ratio of the possible braking area to the accelerating area. The power output of the turbine is assumed to be constant, and aperiodic effects are neglected.

The change of the load angle $\delta = f(t)$ is calculated for a three-phase short circuit assuming a complete loss of load. For a simple system containing a single station and an infinite bus, a partial loss of load may be dealt with by means of formulae based on the equal-area methods, or by using typical curves. For a complicated system containing several stations, simplified step-by-step methods, which neglect the change of armature reaction, are used.

(b) Design calculations

Calculations of this type are used for designing and operating a system. In these the armature reaction, the variation of the voltage E_d, and the effect of the regulating devices on the exciter voltage are usually taken into account. In most cases it is also essential to include the influence of the load, making use of its transient characteristics.

The change of the turbine torque due to variation of the speed or to the action of the speed-regulator is either neglected or considered only approximately. Excitation regulators of the ordinary type may be dealt with by the equal-area method. Forced excitation regulators require more detailed consideration. In these calculations saturation in the generator is usually neglected, as well as pulsating torques due to negative sequence currents and the asymmetrical component of the stator current. Sometimes these effects are approximately allowed for by introducing an additional component of braking torque, acting during the fault and reducing the acceleration.

The margin of safety is usually determined from the amount by which the maximum power can be increased.

(c) Exact calculations

Calculations of this type are performed to check the performance of protective gear in existing systems, to scrutinize the assumptions made in the design, to refine the design calculations in their final stage, or, most of all, to investigate the effect of any modification introduced into systems which contain long lines and work with very low margins of safety. Many factors, considered negligible in the calculations of the previous two classes, are included. The most important of these is the braking effect due to the presence of pulsating torques.

Whichever of these types of calculation is made, the effect of the excitation regulator must always be considered, since the excitation is forced during the first swing.

When making an approximate calculation applying the equal-area criterion, the stability margin k_{st} is assessed by computing the value of the ratio of the possible braking area to the actual acceleration area,

$$k_{st} = \frac{\int_{\delta_{el}}^{\delta_{max}} \Delta P d\delta}{\int_{\delta_0}^{\delta_{cl}} \Delta P d\delta} \, ,$$

where δ_{cl} is the angle at which the fault is cleared.

In more accurate calculations the stability margin can be determined in one of the following three ways:

(*a*) Arbitrarily, from the maximum and initial values of the load angle

$$k_{st} = \frac{180° - \delta_{max}}{\delta_0} \, ,$$

where $\delta_{max} < 180°$

(*b*) By taking a gradual increase in load until stability is lost

$$P_1 = P_0 \, ; \quad P_2 = 1.05 \, P_0 \, ; \quad P_3 = 1.10 \, P_0 \, ; \quad \text{etc.}$$

If P_n is the first load for which the system is unstable,

$$k_{st} = \frac{P_n - P_0}{P_0} \, .$$

(*c*) By considering a gradual decrease of the voltage at the receiving end until stability is lost while transmitting the power P_0,

$$V_1 = V_0 \, ; \quad V_2 = 0.98 \, V_0 \, ; \quad V_3 = 0.96 \, V_0 \, ; \quad \text{etc.}$$

If V_n is the first voltage for which the system is unstable,

$$k_{st} = \frac{V_0 - V_n}{V_0} \, .$$

In calculations dealing with asynchronous operation and resynchronization the analysis of the system must always include:

(*a*) A check of the active power consumed during steady-state asynchronous operation, and of the active power produced by the generator when it is falling out of synchronism.

(*q*) A determination of the stability of the steady-state asynchronous operation, and of the possibility of bringing about automatic resynchronization.

These calculations are made in order to decide on reliable means of returning the system back to synchronism, rather than to determine the performance in detail.

4.3. The Application of Analysers, Models, and Computers to Power System Calculations

The material discussed so far in this book indicates clearly that, in spite of the considerable number of simplifying assumptions and approximations, the mathematical analysis of complicated power systems is a difficult matter. The difficulties are encountered both in setting up the initial differential equations and in solving them, and the resulting calculations are very laborious.

The method of small oscillations when applied to check the steady-state stability of a system containing several stations with automatic excitation control requires the solution of a set of linear equations involving many unknowns. The resulting characteristic equation for a system of only two or three stations may have an order as high as the 16th to 24th, leading to difficult calculations which require a great deal of time.

Calculations connected with transient processes, initiated by sudden changes of operational conditions (studies of transient stability), require much careful work when a step-by-step method is used to solve the non-linear equations. Even an experienced calculator may need 400–500 hours to carry out an analysis of transient stability of a simple system containing two controlled stations and a load.

The complexity of the calculations increases so much with a larger number of stations that it becomes impossible to apply the analytical methods by ordinary manual computation. Still greater difficulties arise when newly-designed components, untried in practice, are introduced in the design of a new installation. The analytical expressions describing the behaviour of such components are not often established with precision. Even if accurate information is available, it becomes hopeless to attempt to formulate the necessary set of equations, allowing for a large number of terms with non-linear coefficients varying in a complicated manner. The time involved in attempting such a solution would make it prohibitive in practice.

Nevertheless, such problems arise and require an engineering solution. Two examples may be mentioned: the behaviour of protective gear designed for a complicated power system which is itself dependent on the operational conditions, and the operation of new types of excitation regulator.

At first sight it would seem that direct experimentation on the actual installation might provide a solution. The opportunities for such work are, however, extremely limited. In spite of the great value of the experimental data obtained in this manner, the practical engineer rarely dares to avail himself of the opportunities that arise, because of the danger of serious damage. And yet the fault conditions are often just what he wishes to investigate.

The way out lies in the application of methods of investigation using physical and mathematical models of all kinds, or high-speed digital computers. The use of mathematical and physical models is already firmly established in the design of electric power systems and in the related experimental work. The analytical study is facilitated by the use of physical models, which are of great value in helping to formulate the equations describing the process under investigation. Mathematical models, in their turn, remove many difficulties arising in the solution of such equations by ordinary means. In the very near future digital computers will also certainly be widely used.

Whatever the method, it must be emphasized, that it is necessary to establish the system equations. Even when the actual component under test can be directly connected to the model, its action must still be described in analytical terms.

However, a physical model may be brought into use as soon as the physical nature of the process is clear and the equations governing the elements of the system are available, while mathematical models require much more detailed knowledge. Before using them, it is necessary to formulate a definite set of equations, to decide on the boundary conditions, and to put the equations into a suitable form for solution.

The theory underlying the use of mathematical and physical models and their practical application to the solution of electrical problems, has been fully worked out during the past few years.

The methods of analysis and of experiment are based on the principle of similarity and require that the equations are written in dimensionless form, so that the results are directly applicable to the full-scale system.

Physical models can be divided into complete models, which represent the process correctly both in space and in time, and into partial models, giving correct representation only in space, or only in time (e.g. field and circuit models used in electrical studies).

To clarify the respective positions occupied by physical and mathematical models as investigation tools, it is worth while to emphasize that physical models are used for basic experimentation, and as a means of extending the validity of experimental results, obtained on a single test equipment, to a wider field. Thus the principle of similarity is important not only in work with models but also in experimentation on actual installations.

Mathematical models, on the other hand, are employed to speed up mathematical calculations carried out on the basis of established equations with known initial and final conditions.

Nevertheless, there is no essential conflict between the physical and mathematical models, as there is not and cannot be any conflict between experiment and analysis.

For the study of any condition within a system which can be simulated, the problems to be solved may be formulated as follows:

A mathematical model is constructed in order to ease the analytical labour involved in a study or a design of an electrical power system. Such a model may be looked upon as belonging to a class of calculating machines. It may take the form of an a.c. network analyser, in which selected resistive and reactive elements represent the network of the system, while the generators or the stations feeding it are represented by means of transformers. The physical processes taking place within the system are not reproduced. Such a model represents to some scale the equivalent circuit of the system to be studied, based on the equations adopted for the solution, and on the configuration of the real system. The magnitudes of the currents, of the voltages, and of the power determined by means of the analyser constitute, within the initial assumptions, a description of the behaviour of the real system. Thus a mathematical model is used to solve a set of equations and to obtain a definite answer, the validity of which is limited by the initial assumptions.

For the design and investigation of very simple power systems, in which the phase displacement between the voltages of the various stations is not important, it is often possible to use d.c. network analysers (calculations on local distribution networks, normal load studies, short-circuit calculations).

With the a.c. network analyser a greater variety of problems can be solved, for example:

(1) current and power distribution in a complicated system under normal, and under fault, conditions,

(2) determination of voltages at various points of the system,

(3) determination of the steady-state stability margin for different conditions of operation,

(4) determination of the margin of transient stability of systems under various fault conditions,

(5) investigation of voltage, current, and power transients in generators, sub-stations, and transmission lines, and the associated analysis of protective gear operation,

(6) analysis of the operation of automatic control devices, and calculation of over-voltages caused by sudden loss of load or other transient occurrences.

Application of physical models

In recent years the factories of the Soviet Union have produced small model machines of special design, which can be used to construct dynamic models of power systems. These machines have outputs of 12–25kW and operate at 220–400 V. Several research and teaching institutions are equipped with physical models of power systems, representing both a.c. systems, and inverter-operated d.c. systems. [16,17,18]

In models of this kind only the power elements are reproduced on a micro-scale. All auxiliary devices, such as protective relays, regulators for the control of excitation, frequency, or power transfer, appear as normal full-scale equipment.

If a model were operated with a different time-scale, i.e. at a different frequency from that of the actual system, the auxiliary devices would also have to be modelled. This added complication would reduce the usefulness of the model, and, consequently, model equipment operating at normal frequency is preferred in practice.

Physical models are used to check the basic theoretical assumptions and the accuracy of the formulae used in calculations; to test the operation of an installation under critical conditions; to try out new ways of transmitting energy; to determine the general behaviour of the system when the parameters are subject to change; to study the electromagnetic, electro-mechanical, and wave-propagation transients, associated with induced over-voltages and lighting surges on transmission lines.

The physical model makes it possible to simulate some occurrence taking place in the actual system, and to subject it to an experimental investigation. It is a miniature copy of the actual system; all its elements (generators, transformers, transmission lines, motors and lighting loads) are physical analogues of the elements of the actual system. In order to attain the desired similarity, the parameters of the model are made proportional to the respective parameters of the original system. The physical model can also be used to examine the assumptions underlying the basic equations, and to study the physical nature of the phenomena.

To construct a physical model in accordance with the principle of similarity, it is necessary first to establish similarity criteria, from which the relations between the parameters of the model and the actual system can be determined. The similarity criteria are established on the basis of the equations describing the operation of the various elements of the system.

Physical models have been applied to the analysis of the operation of electrical power systems in order to gain the precise information which is very important and, in fact, essential for the design and operation both of the system as a whole and of its component parts. They help to establish the optimum design and operating conditions of a given system, and to devise means for its proper control.

But the real problem which must be tackled with the aid of various automatic devices has a far greater generality. It is, in fact, the complete automation of system control. In its broadest terms this problem may be stated as follows:

A given system exists to turn out a certain product; in the present case, electrical energy. When put into operation, the system performs the task entrusted to it, but because of various internal and external disturbances its behaviour inevitably differs from that prescribed. Thus, despite the fact that the system has all the necessary technological resources, its behaviour in service departs from the ideal. In order to obtain satisfactory operation over a long period of time, it is necessary to apply corrective action in a systematic manner at the points which control the flow of materials and of energy. To accomplish this, special control devices have to be incorporated in the system.

4.4. Automatic Control of Power Systems by means of Digital Computers

The application of computers for controlling the operation of power systems is being discussed in the Soviet Union at the present time. It appears that some measure of automatic control of power systems during steady-state operation is practicable and desirable. Although the methods of using computers for this purpose have still to be worked out, it is worth while to consider briefly some of the possibilities.[19, 20, 21, 22]

Control of the steady-state operation implies that optimum conditions of operation are maintained by controlling the voltage, frequency, and power transfer in a super-grid, combining into a single unit all the power systems of the country.

The maintenance of optimum conditions in a unit of such complexity is most essential from the economic point of view. They can hardly be attained by manual operation, even with a large number of control personnel, since the operational conditions differ greatly over such a huge area.

Computers may be used to calculate the most economic distribution of the load. These calculations are based on data about the cost of fuel, the relative cost of energy production by the various units concerned, the various transmission losses, and the number of units in operation. The results of the computer calculation can be put into effect either manually by orders from the control personnel, or automatically by means of various remote control devices which determine the operation of the generators, switches, etc.

In a number of power systems in the United States digital computers are used for calculating loading schedules, transmission line losses, etc. One such machine computes automatically the load graph, on the basis of which the control personnel set up the most economical load distribution.

The digital machines used for these calculations are of the ordinary universal type. It is obvious that they are less well adapted for power-system control than specially designed machines would be. At the time of writing (1958), however, no such special machines are yet in existence anywhere.

The application of digital machines for controlling transient conditions can be broadly visualized in the following manner: the computer, which receives information about the initial state of the system and about the particular disturbance, solves the necessary differential equations during a time interval considerably shorter than the duration of the transient. Having obtained the solution, the various control devices are actuated by the machine in the most effective manner, thus causing the system to function as desired.

It seems likely, however, that control of the transient behaviour of systems will be achieved more effectively by designing regulators employing computing elements either of the continuously-acting or digital type. Some forced excitation regulators of current design already contain elements which perform integration, single and double differentiation, multiplication, and other mathematical operations. Such methods indicate the trend of future development.

CHAPTER 5

METHODS OF IMPROVING THE POWER-HANDLING CAPACITY AND STABILITY OF TRANSMISSION LINES AND POWER SYSTEMS

5.1. General Statement of the Problem

An electrical power system contains many separate elements, the operational characteristics of which have already been discussed.

Some of these elements, such as turbines, generators with their excitation systems, transformers, transmission lines, synchronous condensers which control the reactive power, and switchgear, form in combination the main structure of the power system.

These elements are essential for the operation of the system. Other elements, without which the system can operate reasonably well, perform various auxiliary functions. Their purpose is to improve the power-handling capacity and the reliability of operation of the system as a whole. Examples of auxiliary elements are: switching stations, banks of static capacitors to compensate for the inductive reactance of transmission lines and other elements, synchronous condensers placed at various intermediate points to improve stability, impedances connected in the transformer neutrals, and special loading resistors for braking the generators when load is thrown off. The special devices provided for synchronization and resynchronization of the generators are also important.

All such elements can be classed as auxiliary not only because the system may operate without them, but also because they can be added after the rest of the system has been completed.

Obviously, the effect produced by the auxiliary equipment must be taken into account when a new system is being designed. The correct choice of the main elements of the system cannot be made without considering the improvement in its operation which can be attained by adding the various auxiliary elements. Careful planning requires that all technical and economic aspects of the problem be considered, and that the cost of the auxiliary equipment is balanced against the expected improvement in the operation of the system as a whole.

158

The auxiliary devices and other means used to improve the operational characteristics of a system may be classified under two headings:

(*a*) means of improving the general power-handling capacity and reliability of a system,

(*b*) means provided specially for the improvement of the steady-state or the transient stability of a system.

The transient stability is improved by a decrease of the rupturing time of circuit breakers, by an increase of machine inertia, by connecting resistance or impedance in the transformer neutrals, and by using special load resistors. These measures may also affect indirectly the steady-state stability of the system, making it necessary to readjust the setting of the excitation regulators.

Some other measures, e.g. the operation of switching stations, improve both the transient and the steady-state stability of the system during the period immediately following a fault.

Among the measures for improving the transient stability which operate during or immediately after the fault, some serve to limit the load to be dropped, while other compensate for the load which has been actually disconnected (e.g. either a decrease of the turbine output under fault conditions, or the introduction of special load resistors to absorb the excess output of the generator, and reduce the effect of the drop in the load).

Apart from the use of additional equipment, there are various operational procedures which improve the reliability of the system or reduce the duration of abnormal operation. Such procedures may be initiated manually by the operating staff, or they may be carried out automatically by special equipment, which is not usually very expensive.

Operational procedures of this kind include the following: disconnexion of some of the generators when they are in danger of losing stability; measures for bringing about resynchronization after asynchronous operation, switching of reactors; sub-division of the system into parts not in synchronism with each other; automatic reclosing without loss of synchronism; and self-synchronization by switching in machines without accurate synchronizing.

When any of the various measures are considered, it is essential to have in mind the possibilities of an extensive use of automatic processes by means of which optimum conditions of operation and stability can be achieved economically.

It must be realized that some of the means mentioned above may affect the operation of the system as a whole, or that the operation of its parts under certain transient conditions may bring about undesirable results in some respects. Thus, for example, improved steady-state and transient stability attained by reducing the reactances x_d, x_d', x_d'', x_q'' leads to increased short-circuit currents in the generators, an aspect which must be taken into account at the design stage.

In order to select the best methods of improving the operation of a system, an engineer must not base his decisions on ready-made formulae or solutions. He must make a truly creative effort in order to analyse the complicated phenomena before him in full detail, and to assess the conditions both from the technological and the economic points of view.

5.2 Operational Procedures for Improving the Stability and Reliability of a System

The remainder of this chapter deals with methods of improving stability which involve very little extra cost. They require certain changes in the system circuits and some automatic control devices, and they can be introduced either initially in the design stage, or subsequently into a system already in operation.

The operations considered are mainly those which, in a manually-controlled system, would normally be undertaken by the operating staff when a transient disturbance occurs.

The control room of a power system forms its nerve centre, and issues orders controlling the entire operation of the system. The various operations can be classified as follows:

(a) Sharing of the active and reactive components of load between the various power stations constituting the system. The economics of the operation, the provision of adequate reserves of power, and the steady-state and transient stability, are all matters which must be given due attention.

(b) Control of the frequency of the system, and maintenance of the voltage at various points.

(c) Control of the power flow through the distribution network of the system.

(d) Control of the switching operations along the transmission lines and at the power stations.

(e) Bringing into service, or taking out of service for repair, or for holding in reserve, any given generating set, section of the system, or a complete power station.

(f) Adjustment of the settings of protective relays and other automatic devices in the system.

(*g*) Measures necessary for dealing with faults at the power stations, along main transmission lines, and generally throughout the high voltage distribution network.

All problems arising in connexion with the control of power systems under normal or under fault conditions of operation must be studied from the point of view of maintaining stability and limiting the shock due to sudden changes (e.g. by reducing the magnitude of short-circuit currents).

The reliability of operation should be checked by determining the conditions for transient stability, by ensuring that the margin of steady-state stability is adequate for operation after the fault, by calculating the power distribution after the fault, and making sure that the short-circuit currents are safely limited and that the protective and automatic gear functions correctly.[23]

In the design of a distribution network of a power system the concept of its "stiffness" describes one of its most important properties. The stiffness of the network at any of its nodal points is defined in terms of the change of load required to produce a certain change of the magnitude and phase of the voltage, calculated on a per-unit basis.

The stiffness of the network depends on the relative values of the impedances joining its nodal points. The less dependent on the load are the magnitude and phase of the voltages at the nodal points, the stiffer is the system. It is evident that nodal points located near an infinite bus have a maximum degree of stiffness. A stiff network is advantageous from the point of view of improved steady-state stability and ease of operation of the system after the occurrence of a fault. It has the disadvantage that short-circuit currents are greater and that the total power developed after short-circuit may exceed the rupturing capacity of the circuit-breakers, which is inadmissible.

A stiff network may also lead to difficulty in maintaining transient stability. Difficulties arise, for example, when heavily overloaded lines are connected in parallel. There may also be trouble in the operation of protective gear, making it imperative to employ more elaborate schemes of protection.

Thus the choice of the operational conditions of a system and of its interconnexions is determined by a number of mutually dependent factors.[23]

In applying automation to the solution of problems of system control as a powerful means of increasing the reliability and stability of the

system, it is important that the devices used must not be unduly complicated. Otherwise, although stability may be improved, reliability is likely
to suffer.

5.3. Methods of Connexion of Power Systems

The connexion scheme of the whole power system and of its constituent parts has an important influence on its transient behaviour and
stability.

Certain methods of combining together several power systems, which
increase the stiffness, lead to an increase of the short-circuit currents and
to a need for a greater rupturing capacity of the circuit-breakers.

It is difficult to determine the best operational conditions for any system
because of contradictory requirements, which depend on economics,
reliability, steady-state and transient stability, limitation of short-circuit
currents, etc.

The need to limit the short-circuit currents has become acute because
of a very rapid increase in the power which has to be dissipated during
a short-circuit in a modern power system. It may be necessary to consider
sectionalizing the system if the rupturing capacity of the circuit-breakers
is inadequate. Thus a system having a capacity greater than 1000 MW must
be sectionalized if the rupturing capacity of the circuit breakers is 2500 MVA
otherwise 5000 MVA circuit breakers would become necessary.[23]

The scheme of connexions of long transmission lines also has an important effect on the nature of the transients and on the stability of the
system.

Long transmission lines are of two kinds. A line may connect a remote
power station to a load distribution area. Such a line is required to carry
the whole or the major part of the energy generated at the remote station.
On the other hand, a line may serve as a connecting link between different
systems. Such a line may be required to carry power in either direction,
the amount of power being much less than the total power developed
in any of the interconnected systems.

Transmission lines may also be classified in another way. They may
be purely interconnecting lines, without any sub-stations delivering power
to the area over which they pass (Fig. 5.1 (*a*)), or they may be connected
to local power systems to which they either deliver power, or receive any
available surplus power (Fig. 5.1(*b*)).

Lines with intermediate sub-stations have an advantage from the point
of view of maintaining stability. It is possible to install synchronous con-

densers at such sub-stations, in order to maintain constant voltage at several key points along the line and thereby to improve its stability.

Transmission networks may be arranged in separate sections (Fig. 5.1(*c*)) or, alternatively with, interconnexions (Fig. 5.1(*d*)).

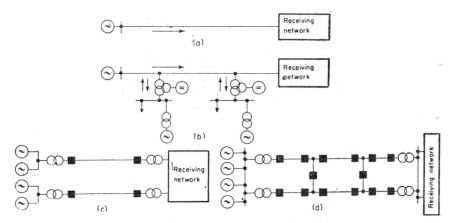

FIG. 5.1. Transmission networks. (*a*) interconnecting line without sub-stations; (*b*) line with intermediate sub-stations; (*c*) transmission network with separate sections; (*d*) transmission network with interconnexions.

A fault along a line connected separately takes out of service the whole of the line as well as all the generators connected to it, i.e. a complete section. Hence the power rating of any section must not exceed the reserve capacity of the system; otherwise normal operation becomes impossible when a fault occurs. Taking a whole section out of service leads to a drop of the frequency of the system, and a possible loss of steady-state stability. It may be necessary to disconnect some of the consumers, or to divide the system into a number of parts not in synchronism with each other.

If there are interconnecting feeders, the faulty section of the transmission line may be isolated and the whole of the power generated by the remote station can be transmitted through the remaining part of the network.

On the other hand, transient stability is more readily maintained in a system with separate lines. A short-circuit occurring at the bus-bars of one of the stations, i.e. at the most critical point of the system (the feeding end of one of the sections), does not in the least affect the transient stability of the other sections, so that no special remedial measures are required. The generators of the faulty section are in any case disconnected, so that the question of maintaining their transient stability does not arise. If a short circuit occurs near the receiving end of the system, it is easy to maintain the transient stability of the unaffected sections. But the favourable conditions for transient stability are paid for by the loss of a part of the generating capacity of the distant station.

Separately connected lines also give rise to some difficulties when the system is to be extended by the addition of other sections. Without going into detailed discussion of these difficulties, it may be mentioned here that separately connected systems are not regarded favourably in the Soviet Union, despite the fact that they have certain advantages. The largest modern systems, like that at Kuibyshev (Fig. 5.2) use transmission lines with interconnecting feeders.

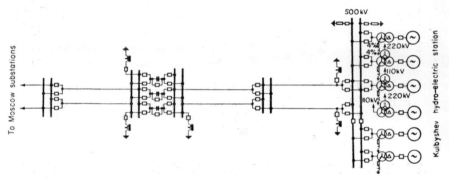

F_{IG}. 5.2. 500 kV transmission link Kuibyshev–Moscow.

For an analysis of the connexion scheme of a power system the location of the point at which a load with a given characteristic is to be connected is very important. Thus a load connected to the bus-bars of a remote station, supplying most of its generated power to the system, may affect stability to some extent.

If forced excitation is used, the operation depends on the connexion of the current transformers feeding the measuring elements of the automatic regulator. If these transformers are so connected that the whole of the generated current is used to actuate the regulator, the regulator setting must be altered when the load changes. Thus, for a current-actuated regulator using time derivatives, the gain coefficients of the corresponding regulator elements must be adjusted. If, on the other hand, the regulator current transformers carry only the component of the main current supplied to the distant receiving end of the system, the regulator settings do not require any readjustment when the amount or the location of the load is altered.

It follows, therefore, that the presence of any load in the system, its magnitude and possible variation, make certain demands on the regulating equipment and affect the nature of the transients in the system.

Sub-division of power systems as a means of maintaining transient stability

The sub-division of a power system into several parts not in synchronism with each other may be considered as a means of preventing the loss of transient stability. Nevertheless, such sub-division, even under fault conditions, must be regarded as highly undesirable. Sub-division invariably leads to weakness, since a deficiency of power may arise in a part of the system and bring about a drop of frequency and of voltage. System subdivision can only be advised as a last resort, when there remains no other way of maintaining transient stability.

Provision should be made in any power system for such subdivision as may be carried out without undue sacrifice. Figure 5.3 illustrates the

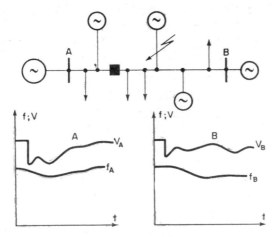

Fig. 5.3. Transient in a system with correctly-designed sub-division.

behaviour under transient conditions of a system which is correctly divided, and Fig. 5.4 where the sub-division is unsatisfactory.

The modern method of re-establishing normal operation of the system by re-combining its parts is to reclose the switches automatically without accurate synchronizing.

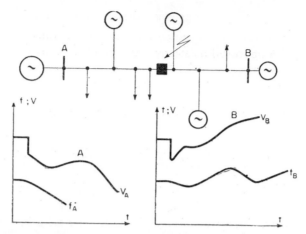

FIG. 5.4. Transient in a system with poorly-designed sub-division.

The effect of the reserve of power on the stability

For reliable operation there must be suitable reserves both in the power stations and elsewhere in the system.

The transient conditions depend mainly on the reserves available at the power stations, since these determine the stability level and the magnitude of the short-circuit currents.

The reserves available at the power stations may be divided into those required for emergency, extra load (to maintain the frequency), overhaul, and for adjustments determined mainly by economic considerations.

For the purposes of this discussion the interest is restricted to the available reserve of rotating machines, required to prevent a shut-downa of the system when a major unit is suddenly taken out of service.

The minimum permissible reserve is determined by the probability of occurrence of the most serious faults. Its amount depends on the connexion scheme, on the method of excitation control, and on the automatic switchgear available to throw-off load. Automatic excitation regulators, for example, increase the margin of available reactive power, making it possible to maintain an overload for a certain period of time by forcing the excitation.

A reserve of active power possessed by the generators improves both the steady-state and transient stability of the system, because the generators then operate at small values of the load-angle δ. On the other hand, to attempt to gain a reserve of reactive power by under-loading the generators under normal conditions leads to a deterioration of stability, since the machines are then under-excited and operate with large initial values of load angle.

Increase of stability by disconnecting generators or reactors

A reduction of the active power output of a generator for a given value of the exciting current is to some extent equivalent to a power reserve beneficial to the stability of the system. If some generators are disconnected when transient changes occur during or immediately after a fault, the stability of the remaining generators is improved. Figure 5.5 shows that the decrease of the active power when some alternators are disconnected exceeds the normal drop in the power during the fault and post-fault periods. Because of this, as seen from Fig. 5.5, the acceleration area becomes smaller and the retardation area greater, thus improving the stability.

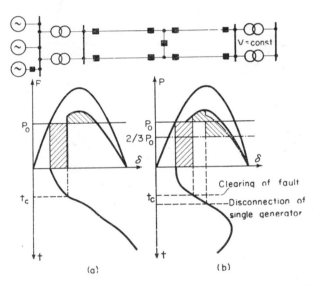

(a)   (b)

Fig. 5.5. Improvement of transient conditions brought about by disconnecting some of the alternators. Acceleration and retardation areas, and the relation $\delta = f(t)$ during a transient: (a) without disconnecting any of the alternators; (b) with some alternators disconnected following a fault, t_c, instant at which the fault is cleared.

Disconnexion of some of the alternators can also be used as a means of synchronizing stations operating asynchronously (resynchronization). Thus, in an experiment carried out on a large hydro-electric station feeding into a long transmission line, it was found possible to regain synchronization by disconnecting 3 generators out of 12, whereas without this manoeuvre the transient conditions were unfavourable and resynchronization was not possible.

Transient stability may be improved by disconnecting some or all of the shunt reactors. The presence of shunt reactors in the radial transmission system shown in Fig. 5.6 improved its steady-state stability. It also

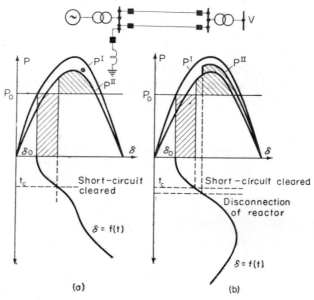

FIG. 5.6. The effect of a shunt reactor and of its disconnexion on the stability. Acceleration and retardation areas, and the relation $\delta = f(t)$ during a transient caused by a short circuit: (*a*) without disconnexion of reactors; (*b*) with reactors disconnected.

proved beneficial under fault conditions by relieving the generators of the need to supply capacitive reactive power (leading current), and making it possible for them to operate with lagging current and, consequently, at a high voltage. On the other hand, the presence of shunt reactors leads to an increase of the transfer impedance between the distant station and the receiving end, and thereby adversely affects the stability. However, the effect of working at a higher voltage is usually beneficial.

If the shunt reactors are disconnected during normal steady operation, an immediate decrease of generated voltage is imperative. Otherwise an inadmissibly high voltage would appear across the step-up transformers and along the transmission line. But during and after a fault, when the line voltage is less than normal, the removal of shunt reactors markedly improves the stability of the system by reducing the transfer impedance and by increasing the line voltage. A slight over-voltage for a short time does not endanger the insulation of the transformers and of the line, but can be of positive benefit from the point of view of stability.

The above remarks regarding the beneficial effect of disconnecting some of the generators or reactors should not be interpreted as a recommendation. These methods of improving stability are less desirable than the other methods. The removal of some of the generators brings about a decrease of the generated power and makes it necessary to resynchronize the disconnected machines and pick up the load. Disconnexion of the reactors involves less difficulty, but it is not an advisable operation because of the danger of over-voltage and the need for re-connexion when normal operation is re-established.

5.4. Operation out of Synchronism as a Means of Improving the Resultant Stability

Asynchronous operation of generators

If a generator, after falling out of synchronism, is not disconnected from the system, its operation takes on a new character. Usually it begins

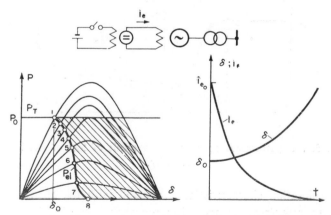

Fig. 5.7. Asynchronous operation caused by loss of excitation. 1–8 — gradual decrease of generated power due to loss of excitation; P_T—turbine power; P_{el}—generated power.

to act as an asynchronous machine, operating at a speed slightly higher than synchronous, and supplies active power to the system. Asynchronous operation may be initiated by several causes, such as loss of excitation (Fig. 5.7), loss of transient stability after a sudden disturbance (Fig.5.8), or a loss of steady-state stability when under-excited in a heavily-loaded system (Fig. 5.9).

In the first case the generator operates entirely as an asynchronous machine (though in salient-pole machines there may be a synchronous power component due to saliency); in the second and third cases the generator, when excited, produces pulsating synchronous as well as asynchronous power.

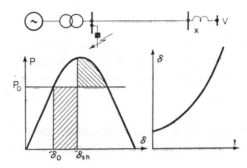

FIG. 5.8. Asynchronous operation caused by a shock resulting in loss of transient stability; δ_{sh} change of load angle due to a sudden shock.

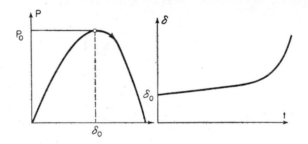

FIG. 5.9. Asynchronous operation as a result of loss of steady-state stability.

The acceleration characteristics associated with the change from synchronous to asynchronous operation are shown in Fig. 5.10.

If a generator were to operate asynchronously with a value of slip of 2–4 per cent or more, there would be a large rotor current causing rotor heating and appreciable mechanical stresses. Because of this, it has long been taken as axiomatic that asynchronous operation is inadmissible, and that a machine which has lost synchronism must be immediately disconnected.

The work done in the U. S. S. R. in 1945–50 under the direction of Prof. T. A. Syromyatnikov, has proved, however, that asynchronous operation over short periods is free from danger for most synchronous machines. Turbo-generators can operate asynchronously during long periods of time, developing a power of the order of the normal rating. The slip is of the order of a few tenths of one per cent and the currents are in no way dangerous to the machine.

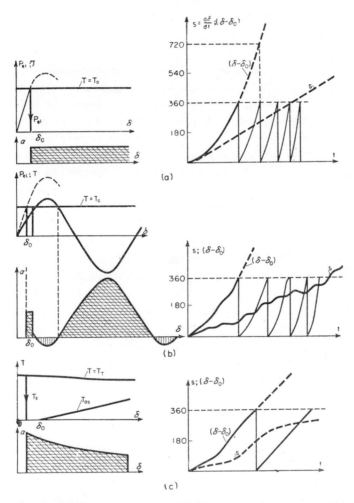

FIG. 5.10. Characteristics illustrating different ways of losing synchronism; (acceleration a, load angle δ, slip s). (a) $P_s = 0$; $\Delta T = T_t = \text{const}$; (b) $P_s = f(\delta)$; (c) $T_s = 0$; $T_{as} = f(\delta)$.

Asynchronous operation of a number of generators, or of a single machine of appreciable output, may be thought inadmissible because of its effect on the stability of the system. This argument is based on the fact (as explained in Chapter 2), that an asynchronously operating generator takes a considerable amount of reactive power from the system, thereby causing a large voltage drop in the whole system. The stability of the remaining generators and induction motors is thus endangered, and conditions favourable to a collapse of voltage are created.

This difficulty has become far less likely nowadays in the Soviet Union. Automatic regulation and forced excitation have been incorporated in all stations, thus making it possible to supply reactive power to any generator (or even a whole station) operating asynchronously and yet to maintain a voltage within the system which is sufficiently close to normal. It is possible to maintain such operation for short periods, and occasionally even during relatively long periods. It has been found possible in practice to return the system to normal operation, even though a generator which has fallen out of synchronism may operate asynchronously for some time. Since in such circumstances the supply to the consumers is not interrupted, it can certainly be claimed that the resultant stability of the system has been maintained.

Nevertheless, since asynchronous operation is abnormal for the equipment of the system, it should not be allowed without prior analysis and verification. It is helpful to consider for this purpose the asynchronous operation of a generator which has lost its excitation.[24]

With falling exciting current in the generator the flux and the electromagnetic torque also diminish. The excess of the mechanical torque provided by the turbine causes the machine to accelerate and to fall out of synchronism (Fig. 5.7). The power output of the turbine falls with increase of speed because the action of the speed regulator closes the inlet valve and reduces the intake of steam (or of water). Hence the power output of the under-excited machine is always less than that at normal excitation.

The reactive power required to set up the electromagnetic field in the machine can only be supplied by the system. The stator currents increase due to the reactive power required for asynchronous operation, and they fluctuate about a mean value at a frequency of $2 (f_0 - f_s)$. Asynchronous operation can be readily detected from the oscillation of the pointer of the stator-current ammeter. The number of pulsations per second α_1 of the pointer is numerically equal to the value of slip expressed in per cent ($f_0 = 50$ c/s)

$$s = \frac{\omega_0 - \omega_s}{\omega_0} \cdot 100 = \frac{f_0 - f_s}{f_0} \cdot 100 = \frac{\dfrac{\alpha_1}{2} \cdot 100}{50} = \alpha_1 \,.$$

The amplitude of oscillation of the stator currents is least when the excitation winding is open, while the slip is less when the excitation winding is closed.

The maximum active power output of the machine depends on the maximum permissible value of the stator current, which is increased during asynchronous operation because of the large reactive power component. If asynchronous operation is to be tolerated over a longer period of time, the permissible output of active power is of the order of 50–60 per cent of the nominal. Higher outputs are permissible if the heavy stator currents flow only for a short time.

When the excitation is re-applied, the generator pulls smoothly into synchronism, and there is no reason to fear any damage to the machine, provided that it does not remain unexcited too long.

The operational instructions issued by the Soviet Ministry of Power Stations[24] are based on this fact. They lay down that the operating staff should not disconnect a generator that has lost its excitation, but should take immediate action to restore it.

Turbo-generators which have lost their excitation (assuming the discharge resistance to be connected to the winding) can continue to operate if the machine is not otherwise faulty. If the stator current exceeds the rated value, the machine must be relieved of some of its load, and when the cause of the loss of excitation has been discovered, it must be restored, if necessary by connecting the field winding to an emergency source of excitation.

It is permissible to allow a turbo-generator which has lost its excitation to operate asynchronously for about 15–30 min. If the excitation is not restored during this period, the machine should be taken out of service. If the machine which has lost excitation is otherwise faulty, or if its excitation winding is down to earth, it should be taken out of service immediately.

Asynchronous operation is inadmissible if the rotor losses exceed the normal value, or if the stator current exceeds the normal maximum value by over 10 per cent. For hydro-generators asynchronous operation is permissible for rather shorter periods than for turbo-generators.

Possibilities of resynchronization

By permitting asynchronous operation, caused either by loss of excitation or by loss of stability, it becomes possible to reduce the loss of output during the period after a fault before synchronization is restored. If a machine which has lost synchronism is first disconnected and then resynchronized, it is likely that the full-load output cannot be restored for about 20–60 minutes. On the other hand, if asynchronous operation is allowed, there is no complete loss of output, but only a temporary reduction.

If steady-state stability is lost as a result of a change of connexions of the system or of an overload on the generators, resynchronization is possible only after the causes of instability have been removed by the operating staff.

Resynchronization after a loss of transient stability can take place under manual control, or be brought about automatically under all conditions by speed regulators, or by specially-designed synchronizing gear.

The problem of automatic resynchronization has been under discussion for several decades. P. S. Zhdanov and V. I. Ivanov (1932–35), and more recently, I. A. Syromyatnikov, have repeatedly called attention in their papers to the fact that loss of transient stability under fault conditions is much more frequent than is commonly believed. In some cases a generator, or even a whole station, having lost synchronism, regains it as soon as the short-circuit is removed, or after a few cycles of oscillation. This oscillation is not always recognized for what it is, namely asynchronous operation, and may sometimes be completely overlooked.

Tests carried out on the Kuibyshev–Moscow system have fully proved that successful resynchronization is possible not only for single generators, but also for sections of systems, even when they contain long transmission lines.

Self-synchronization and automatic reclosing without accurate synchronizing

By self-synchronization is understood the series of operations carried out when a generator is connected to the system without an accurate adjustment of its frequency or of the magnitude and phase of its voltage.

When self-synchronization is attempted, an unexcited synchronous machine running at a speed slightly below synchronism is connected to the supply, and operates at first as an induction motor. This limits the currents flowing in the machine, and prevents over-voltages which would appear if the windings were open circuited. It is recommended that the generator should be connected to the system at a slip of the order of 2–3 per cent, although slips as high as 5–10 per cent can be used without danger. The excitation is applied either at the same instant as the machine is connected, or immediately afterwards, and the entry into synchronous operation is then usually reasonably smooth.

Hydro-generators may sometimes synchronize before the excitation is applied because of the torque due to saliency. This is, as will be shown, an undesirable property. When the generator speed is sub-synchronous, the mechanical torque developed by the prime mover balances the asynchronous and the loss torques. The mean value of the asynchronous torque may be calculated from equations (2.2) or (2.3), the value of slip used being that at which the machine is connected to the system.

The entry into synchronism is particularly easy when the mechanical torque, due to the turbine, and the asynchronous torque act in the same sense after the machine has been connected, and when the magnitude of the asynchronous torque due to the generator is greater than the turbine torque.

In practice, in order to make certain that the machine synchronizes, the turbine torque should not exceed 20 per cent of the mean asynchronous torque developed by the generator at the slip at which the machine is connected. Thus the excess torque ΔT should be of the order of 80 per cent of the asynchronous torque developed. As a rule, synchronization is attempted at a sub-synchronous speed and the excess torque has to accelerate the rotating mass in order to gain synchronism.

It is not difficult to obtain a simple criterion for successful self-synchronization by relating the magnitude of the excess torque to the resulting acceleration of the rotor.

Experiments have shown that for a hydro-generator without damper windings the acceleration should not exceed $0 \cdot 5 – 1 \cdot 0$ cycles/sec^2.

The angular acceleration a can be expressed as:

$$a = \omega_0 \frac{\Delta T}{J},$$

where a is in rad/sec^2, ΔT is the per-unit torque, and J is in seconds.

If the excess torque ΔT is taken to be $\leqslant 0 \cdot 8 \, T_{as}$, and if the angular acceleration in cycles/sec^2 is a_c, the required criterion is

$$a_c = \frac{0 \cdot 8 \cdot T_{as} \cdot f_0}{J},$$

where $f_0 = 50$ c/s.

When calculating the value of the asynchronous torque T_{as}, the effect of the discharge resistance R_d connected to the rotor winding must not be neglected, so that the effective transient time constant $(\tau'_d)_{eff}$ is given by:

$$(\tau'_d)_{eff} = n\tau_{d_0} \cdot \frac{x'_d}{x_d},$$

where $n = \dfrac{R_e}{R_e + R_d}$, R_e being the resistance of the field winding.

To make certain that the above condition is satisfied in practice, and to ease the entry into synchronism, special provision is sometimes made to limit the available acceleration near synchronous speed.

For hydro-generators with damper windings, and for turbo-generators with solid iron rotors, there is no difficulty in obtaining the required acceleration because the asynchronous torque is large.

It was mentioned earlier that hydro-generators may synchronize even when unexcited. This is undesirable because synchronization may take place with incorrect polarity, so that the rotor has to move through 180 electrical degrees when excitation is applied. This displacement is accompanied by quite large oscillations, so that synchronism may sometimes be lost again. Consequently, when the machine is at a relatively low speed it is wise to apply the excitation immediately after switching on.

On the other hand, when a generator is connected to the system at a large value of slip, for example, when automatic re-closing with self-synchronization is used, it is desirable to delay the application of excitation, because otherwise the exciting current may reach its full value before the slip has decreased sufficiently.

An excited machine running asynchronously may take a large current and there may be considerable voltage fluctations in the system, causing trouble both in the system and in the machine being synchronized.

If the excitation is introduced at the right moment, these troublesome effects are less marked, although a certain drop of voltage is inevitable at the instant when the generator is connected to the system. Normally this voltage drop ΔV can be tolerated, its value to a first approximation being given by

$$\Delta V = V_0 - V_1 = V_0 - (\sqrt{3}) \cdot I \cdot x'_{dt} .$$

Even in the most unfavourable conditions, when a large machine is being brought into synchronism with a smaller one, the current in the machine being synchronized falls fairly rapidly, so that the normal voltage is soon re-established.

When it is intended to use the method of self-synchronization, it is important to ensure that the settings of the protective gear used with the motors or transmission lines in the system are such that they do not respond to a voltage drop of short duration brought about by the process of self-synchronization. The automatic speed regulators of the turbines should also be checked, because hunting may occur after self-synchronization if their settings are incorrectly adjusted.

In modern practice self-synchronization is coming into use for generators and synchronous condensers of the largest ratings and is preferable to the method of accurate synchronization for many reasons:

(*a*) Simplicity, since faulty operation is practically impossible.

(*b*) Speed of operation, particularly valuable for dealing with fault conditions.

(*c*) Suitability for automatic control.

(*d*) Possibility of synchronization even at very low, or fluctuating, values of frequency and voltage.

(*e*) Simplification of the operations required for paralleling generators driven by prime movers without automatic speed regulators, or of generators without remote control of main switches.

(*f*) Facility of rapid restoration of the connexions between station and system by using automatic re-closing of the line switches and self-synchronization of each generator in turn, or of all generators together.

The two undesirable features of self-synchronization, as already mentioned, are the current surge and the associated voltage drop which occur when an unexcited generator running at a speed below synchronism is connected to the system.

The initial value of the stator current depends on the position of the rotor at the instant of switching. The current is greatest if the switch closes at the instant when the direct axis of the rotor coincides with the magnetic axis associated with the supply voltage. In this case the alternating component $I_\sim$ of the stator current is:

$$I_\sim = \frac{V}{(\sqrt{3}) \cdot x'_{dt}},$$

where V is the system voltage, and x'_{dt} is the total transient reactance of the generator and line.

The magnitude of the alternating component of the stator current is a useful guide as to whether self-synchronization is permissible or not. Normally it should not be attempted if $I_\sim > 3 \cdot 5 \, I_{\text{nom}}$.

To calculate the value of the current as a function of time with greater precision it is necessary to use the equations due to Gorev and Park, from which i_d and i_q, the direct and quadrature axis current components, can be determined.

The torques acting on the generator rotor during self-synchronization present no kind of danger to the machine. An unsuccessful attempt of accurate synchronization using the standard method, with the machine and system voltage vectors out of phase, is much more dangerous. The resultant torque T produced in such circumstances can be considered to consist approximately of three components:

$$T \simeq T_1 + T_2 + T_3 \,,$$

where

T_1 — torque produced when an unexcited generator is switched on,

T_2 — torque produced during a short-circuit,

T_3 — torque due the interaction of the fields due to the exciting winding and the armature reaction, i.e. the magnetic field set up by the system to which the machine is connected.

Thus the torque T exceeds the torque acting on the rotor during self-synchronization by the amount of the torque $(T_2 + T_3)$. The most unfavourable instant of switching occurs when the machine is connected to an infinite bus ($x_s = 0$) at $\delta_0 = 135°$. The torque $(T_2 + T_3)$ is then about 15 times as great as the normal torque.[25]

REFERENCES

1. I. L. KAGANOV, *Electronic and ionic inverters*, Gosenergoizdat (1955).
2. G. V. ZEVEKE, P. A. IONKIN, A. V. NETUSHIL, S. V. STRAKHOV, *Electrotechnics*, Vols. I and II, Gosenergoizdat (1955).
3. P. S. ZHDANOV, *Stability of electric systems*, Gosenergoizdat (1948).
4. (a) G. N. PETROV, *Electrical machines*, Gosenergoizdat (1938).
   (b) M. P. KOSTENKO, *Electrical machines*, Gosenergoizdat (1945).
   (c) P. S. SERGEYEV, *Electrical machines*, Gosenergoizdat (1955).
5. Yu. E. GARKAVI and M. I. SMIRNOV, *Governing of hydro-electric turbines*, Gostekhizdat (1954).
6. I. A. SYROMYATNIKOV, *Operation of synchronous generators*, Gosenergoizdat (1952).
7. E. W. KIMBARK, *Power system stability*, Vols. I, II, III, Wiley, New York (1948–56).
8. S. B. CRARY, *Power system stability*, Vols. I, II, Wiley, New York (1945–47).
9. A. A. VORONKOV, *Theoretical mechanics*, Gostekhteoretizdat (1954).
10. M. V. MEYEROV, *Introduction to the automatic control of electrical machines*, U.S.S.R. Academy of Sciences Press (1956).
11. Ya. Z. TSYPKIN, *Stability of automatic control systems*, V.Z.E.I. (1953).
12. Ya. Z. TSYPKIN, *Conditions of stability of automatic control systems*, Mashgiz (1951).
13. V. L. LOSYEVSKY, *Automatic control of technological processes*, Oborongiz (1950).
14. A. V. FATEYEV, *Linear theory of automatic control*, Gosenergoizdat (1954).
15. YAN CHAN TSE, Problems of analysis of transient processes associated with automatic excitation control, *Dissertation*, Moscow Power Institute (1956).
16. V. A. VENIKOV, *Development of analytical and laboratory methods of investigation of power-system behaviour as a means of accelerating the introduction of automatic control. Automation of complex industrial processes*, U.S.S.R. Academy of Sciences Press (1957).
17. V. A. VENIKOV and A. V. IVANOV-SMOLENSKY, *Physical models of electrical powet systems*, Gosenergoizdat (1956).
18. I. M. TETEL'BAUM, *Electrical models of physical systems*, Lecture Course, Part I, Moscow Power Institute (1955).
19. E. KOL'MAN, *Cybernetics*, Znaniye Publishing House (1956).
20. V. A. TRAPEZNIKOV, Mathematical models of dynamic systems, *Elektrichestvo*, No. 8 (1955).
21. S. A. LEBEDEV, *Electronic calculating machines*, U.S.S.R. Academy of Sciences Press (1956).
22. N. A. YAVLINSKY, Rapid calculating machines and automation of industrial processes, *Elektrichestvo*, No. 9 (1956).
23. I. M. MARKOVICH, *Power systems and their operation*, Gosenergoizdat (1957).

24. Technical department of the Ministry of Power Stations. Regulations concerning operation of turbo-generators when excitation is lost, *Elektrostantsii*, No. 7 (1950).
25. L. G. MAMIKONYANZ, Electromagnetic torques developed in synchronous machines when connected by the method of self-synchronization, *Elektrichestvo*, No. 8 (1954).

INDEX